£2.50

C000232877

EX LIBRIS

A SUSSEX GUIDE

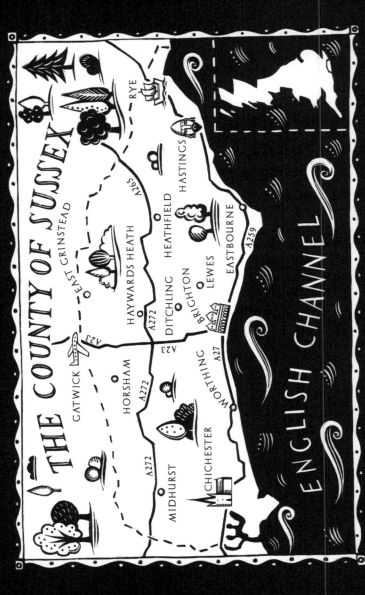

A SUSSEX ALPHABET

ELEANOR FARJEON

INTRODUCED BY
PETER ROBINSON

Illustrated with the original woodcuts by
SHEILA M. THOMPSON

SNAKE RIVER PRESS

SNAKE RIVER PRESS

Book No 20
Books about Sussex for the enthusiast

Published in 2017 by
SNAKE RIVER PRESS
South Downs Way, Alfriston, Sussex BN26 5XW
www.snakeriverpress.co.uk

ISBN 978-1-906022-19-8

This book was designed & produced by
SNAKE RIVER PRESS

ART DIRECTOR & PUBLISHER *Peter Bridgewater*
PAGE MAKEUP *Richard Constable*
CONSULTANT *Lorraine Harrison*
EDITOR *Jennifer Davis*

This book is typeset in Perpetua & Gill Sans,
two fonts designed by Eric Gill

Printed and bound in China

DEDICATION

*To all those who, throughout the generations, have loved
and cherished the county of Sussex*

*With thanks to Anne Harvey & the Eleanor Farjeon Literary Estate;
also Frances Guthrie & the estates of James Guthrie &
Sheila Hamilton for her illustrations*

CONTENTS

INTRODUCTION

'As gardens grow with flowers English grows with words,
Words that have secret powers, Words that give joy like birds.'

ELEANOR FARJEON

Today, Eleanor Farjeon is possibly best known for the lyrics of *Morning Has Broken* (1931), a hymn that was later popularised by Cat Stevens. But for most of the twentieth century, this remarkable, creative writer was a household name to generations of young children for her stories and her poems. So it is both an honour and a delight to revive part of the literary heritage she bequeathed us in *A Sussex Alphabet*, a lasting testament to her very real affection for this extraordinarily rich county.

Eleanor Farjeon was born on 13 February 1881 into a literary and theatrical family.[1] Her father, Benjamin Leopold Farjeon, was a well-known Victorian novelist, and her mother, Maggie Farjeon, was the daughter of the celebrated American actor Joseph Jefferson. Her three brothers, Harry, Joseph and Herbert, were also creative and helped to develop her imaginative capacities.

Eleanor grew up in London, in a loving and creative environment, having free rein of her father's extensive library of some 8,000 volumes and mixing with his coterie of friends. Her childhood was characterised by an imaginative zeal that was mediated through the strange game of 'TAR', an extended game of make-believe, in which the four young Farjeons, led by Harry, assumed the persona of people they met, read about, or had seen on stage. Whether writing for adults or children, 'TAR' was certainly at the root of her fantasy — a genre at which, as one

1. *For details of Eleanor Farjeon's life see the biographical portraits: Eileen H. Colwell,* Eleanor Farjeon *(1961); Denys Blakelock,* Eleanor: Portrait of A Farjeon *(1966); Annabel Farjeon,* Morning Has Broken: A Biography of Eleanor Farjeon *(1986); and an extensive introduction to Eleanor in Anne Harvey's edited collection of her poems,* Like Sorrow or a Tune: Poems by Eleanor Farjeon *(2013). For her autobiographical writings see:* A Nursery in the Nineties *(1935), and to some extent* Edward Thomas: The Last Four Years *(1958).*
2. *Edward Wagenknecht, 'The Little Prince Rides the White Deer: Fantasy and Symbolism in recent Literature',* College English, *vol. 7, no. 8 (May, 1946), p. 433.*
3. *'Books for Holiday Makers'.*

mid-century critic wrote, she had 'no superior in the field'.[2] In all,
throughout a long and productive career, Eleanor published over eighty
books and collections of poems, many of which were reprinted for
successive generations and invariably richly illustrated.

The consistent quality of her prose and verse distinguishes her as one
of the most important children's writers of the twentieth century, a fact
recognised in her own lifetime by several awards: the Carnegie Medal
of the Library Association (1955), the Hans Christian Andersen Award
(1956) and the Regina Medal (1959). Shortly after her death on 5 June
1965, the Eleanor Farjeon Award was created, which honours service to
children's literature and is still recognising literary talent to this day.

Classifying Eleanor's literary output has often been a point of
contention for reviewers, but Ann Spice comes closest to the mark in
an article for *The Listener*. Describing Eleanor's novels as 'books that
refuse to take anything for granted, but dance deliciously in the fields
of fancy', she compared Eleanor with 'that other writer of Sussex
country', her contemporary Sheila Kaye-Smith. But whereas Kaye-Smith
dealt with 'the realities of life on the South Downs and marshes, Martin
Pippin [arguably Farjeon's most famous character] tells the fantasies and
fairy tales that have taken root in that same life'.[3]

Although she never married, Eleanor cultivated a wide network of
literary and artistic friends including D.H. Lawrence, Arthur Ransome
(*Swallows and Amazons*) and the American poet Robert Frost. She also
had a number of intense companionships, most notably with the critic
and poet Edward Thomas and, after his death in 1917, with the married
English teacher George Earle.

Eleanor lived most of her life at number 22 Perrins Walk, Hampstead,
in 'the quaintest little house this side of fairyland', as the *Catholic Herald*
purred in an article published in 1951, soon after her conversion to
Catholicism. So although, during WWI, she lived for two years in the
Sussex village of Houghton, she experienced Sussex predominantly
through summer rambles on which she encountered local characters,
rustic cuisine, unique customs and native flora and fauna, which her
fertile mind wove into countless stories and poems.

Intrepidness is a term very applicable to Eleanor. Yet while for female Victorian writers, like Isabella Bird, this meant gallivanting around the Far East, Eleanor's world was mostly confined to London and the counties traversed by the South Downs. Although it was undoubtedly Edward Thomas who first introduced her to the delights of walking,[4] she immediately realised the literary benefits accruing from such creative foraging and became 'countrified' and an almost habitual rambler. Thus, emerging from an imaginative childhood in her mid-twenties, the sights and sounds of Sussex combined into a rich phantasmagorical world of fairies and virgin maidens, and a lifetime of infectious creativity.

In August 1913 we find Eleanor busy planning a walking tour over the South Downs with writers Viola Meynell and Maitland Radford, from Greatham to Lewes and on to Berwick. In the end, this never took place, but many like it did over the years. Her walks were typically adaptable and would swell and reduce in numbers as they went along, the route often changing upon the receipt of letters. In July 1915 one such letter from Edward Thomas reached her at Aldwick (near Bognor Regis) suggesting that she should divert her course and see his friend, James Guthrie. This short, one-and-a-half-mile detour and the establishment of a long friendship resulted in Guthrie's decision to print *A Sussex Alphabet* some twenty-five years later! This same ramble also generated a particularly evocative description of Eleanor in her Sussex element. While walking in one of the lanes, from Felpham to Guthrie's home in Flansham, Eleanor came across a couple of young scouts 'not long past wolf-cubhood'. Eleanor later described the encounter:

> *I glanced at their kit, and they at mine: haversack, drover's ash stick, and green leather cap with some hedge-leaves pushed into the band. We took each other in, and passed without speaking.* (Edward Thomas, p. 156)

These young scouts were actually two of James Guthrie's sons, Robin and John. However, it is the diary kept by their brother 'Stuart' that

---

4. *Eleanor Farjeon*, Edward Thomas: the Last Four Years, *Oxford: O.U.P. (1979), p. 5.*

reveals the full impression Eleanor made on the children:

> *Miss Farjeon is great fun. She stumps along with her knapsack on her back*
> *and her chalala* [shillelagh?] *in her hand, looking for all the world like*
> *a pilgrim…she lights a pipe sometimes—and talks and shouts and laughs*
> *and turns the place into the very haunt of merriment. She is one of the*
> *most marvellous personalities I know.* (Edward Thomas, p. 158)

The correlation between Eleanor's direct experience of rambling and her poetic and prose composition is nowhere better highlighted than in a slim, six-poem Sussex-related collection titled *All the Way to Alfriston*, which was published in 1918 by the Guthrie 'wolf-cubs' under the 'respectful' imprint of the Greenleaf Press.[5] Revealing the genesis of the poems some years later, Eleanor recalled how in the year 1915, 'as I walked the Downs from Chichester to Alfriston, [I] made a handful of songs on the way, which appeared under the imprint of Greenleaf'.[6] She was nonplussed, however, by the title page illustration drawn by Robin Guthrie in which she was inexplicably (according to her) shown as 'a sort of H.G. Wellsian tramp in check knickerbockers'.[7] However accurate the portrayal, the image is certainly an enduring one! Although in *All the Way to Alfriston* we directly accompany Eleanor on her journey east across the Downs, whereas the *Alphabet* reveals her footsteps in a less linear, random way, many of the characters featured are common to both books, especially shepherds and gypsies, a preoccupation that owes a lot to the imaginative aesthetic of the Pre-Raphaelite brotherhood almost a century before.

In 1930, a long-time correspondent and frequent visitor to Sussex, Helen Dean Fish, who 'walked for two days with Eleanor Farjeon on the Sussex Downs in Martin Pippin country', wrote of the 'amusing rhymes' that Eleanor would make up about her companions.[8] For

---

5. *James Guthrie's press was called the Pear Tree Press, so the Green Leafpress is an acknowledgement both of their father's activity and of their youth and inexperience.*
6. *Edward Thomas, op cit., p. 159.*
7. *Ibid, p.159.*
8. *Eileen H. Colwell,* Eleanor Farjeon, *Bodley Head Monograph (1961), p. 29.*

Eleanor, everything she saw, heard, or felt represented material for self-expression, and as a result, the immediacy of her writing shines through. Although comfortable using a range of poetic forms and variation of voice, her most successful poems are, unquestionably, those written in the first person, giving the prose a compelling immediacy. In *A Sussex Alphabet*, the entry for the letter 'I', 'As I walk Sussex, hill and shore', combines her love of walking in Sussex with this first-person voice, and a lovely fleck of fantasy at the end when Eleanor laments not yet encountering an 'Indian chief'. These three ingredients – direct experience of Sussex, an acute sense of her own voice, and lively humour – combine to produce a highly entertaining formula.

A Sussex Alphabet & All the Way to Alfriston

Nearly a century has passed since Eleanor Farjeon's *A Sussex Alphabet* first appeared, appropriately enough, in the *West Sussex Gazette*. Thereafter, the alphabetical poems were reprinted as part of a slim collection entitled *Tunes of a Penny Piper* (1922). They were set to music in 1924 in one of many fruitful sibling collaborations with her brother Harry Farjeon, composer and later professor at the Royal Academy of Music. Finally, in March 1939 they were published as a richly illustrated limited edition by James Guthrie's great Sussex-based publishing enterprise, the Pear Tree Press. The present resized edition is based on this scarce edition of 220 copies, retaining the exquisite woodcut illustrations by Sheila M. Thompson.

The idea behind *A Sussex Alphabet* is simple but deceptively effective: to use the twenty-six letters of the alphabet to provide the framework for a series of poems, which, taking each letter in turn, celebrate the county of Sussex, utilising place names, local traditions, cultural references, and often Eleanor's unique and witty observations. Eleanor used the alphabet or A.B.C. format extensively and to great success during the 1920s, producing, among others, *The Country Child's Alphabet* (1924), the *Town Child's Alphabet* (1924), *An Alphabet of Magic* (1928) and the *A.B.C. of the BBC* (c.1928). As Eileen Colwell has noted, such recycling and repackaging of content, especially poetic content, was seldom to the detriment of the work and invariably enhanced it.

Those familiar with the South Coast will note with satisfaction that Eleanor's Sussex is very much defined by, to borrow Kipling's evocative phrase, the 'blunt, bow-headed, whale-backed Downs' that form the spine of the county.[9] The poems, ranging considerably in length from two lines to twenty, feature numerous rhyming schemes and meter, and were brought together in the aftermath of WWI. They are very much the result of Eleanor's intense interaction with the South Downs during the numerous stout-sticked and intrepid rambles that played an important role in her relatively late transition from adolescence to adulthood. At times they are light and tinged with playful flippancy – 'X is Chichester Market Cross, If you tell me it's not, I am quite at a loss' – but at other times they are more thoughtful and contemplative, showing her acute powers of observation and lively disposition. They represent more than literary geography, too, testifying that Eleanor had finally come to terms with her profound personal grief over the death of her literary soul mate, the poet Edward Thomas, killed in action at Arras in 1917. She had emerged from her two-year tenancy of a cottage in the picturesque downland village of Houghton, full of creative energy and growing confidence as a poet and author.

A Sussex Alphabet is best read as both complementary to and contrastive with her more sustained and serious-minded poetic work of the same period, All the Way to Alfriston (1918), which is brought together with A Sussex Alphabet in this volume for the first time. The former allows the reader to accompany Eleanor on a long ramble along the South Downs Way from Chichester in the West to the downland village of Alfriston in the East. Eleanor was of course by no means unique in her choice of subject for both works, as Sussex, and especially the South Downs, have provided the inspiration for a long and distinguished list of writers and artists. Eleanor's contemporary Anthony Mario Ludovici, secretary to the sculptor Pierre Auguste Rodin, viewed the South Downs in sensual terms, quite literally as 'vast rolling leagues of wench and hind'.[10] Writing

9. *Rudyard Kipling, 'Sussex', 1902, in* A Choice of Songs from the Verse of Rudyard Kipling, *London: Methuen & Co. Ltd (1925), p. 35.*

10. *Anthony Mario Ludovici, 'The South Downs',* The Saturday Review, *27 January 1917.*

a little earlier in his poem 'Sussex', Kipling saw them as providing a sort of personal, deep-felt rootedness, an eternal and unchanging backdrop, 'The wise turf cloaks the white cliff-edges, As when the Romans came', a place to which the wanderer returns and is spiritually revived. What singles out Farjeon's contribution, however, is her complete rejection of the muse-like personification of the South Downs in purely aesthetic terms, and her desire (also witnessed throughout her prose writing) to populate or 'people' them with the characters she encountered on her many walks and those she dreamt up. The guileless combination of the real and the imaginary is perfectly illustrated in an unpublished letter from Eleanor thanking two local Martin Pippin fans for their interest in her celebrated character, and exuberantly suggesting a short literary pilgrimage: '…if you go right to the bottom, and follow the path to the right, with the river on your left, in five or six minutes you come to the loveliest quarry in the world – but there, I'm sure you know it, and hidden inside it is the hollow where Rosalind hid with the Hart.'[11] The Downs have more than an aesthetic physical presence, for they constantly intervene and shape communities and their way of life. The diversity of the poems within the *Alphabet* recognises and mirrors the great range of environments and customs that compose the Downs, from deep ghylls to windswept hilltops – features that have belatedly received lasting acknowledgement in the recent creation of the South Downs National Park.

Readers who are not Sussex-born, or have little familiarity with the county, might at first find the poems of *A Sussex Alphabet*, with their strong local focus and references, a little confusing and eclectic. Notes have therefore been added at the end of the book to ensure that they are accessible to all.

The poems of *A Sussex Alphabet* and *All the Way to Alfriston* offer a great deal to readers both young and old, local or from afar, and stand the test of time, continuing to stimulate all who stumble upon them while on their own literary ramblings.

---

11. *Eleanor Farjeon, letter to M.E.Whitehorn and E.D. McLeod, 18 June 1924. Quoted with permission of Ruth de Mallet Morgan.*

A SUSSEX
ALPHABET

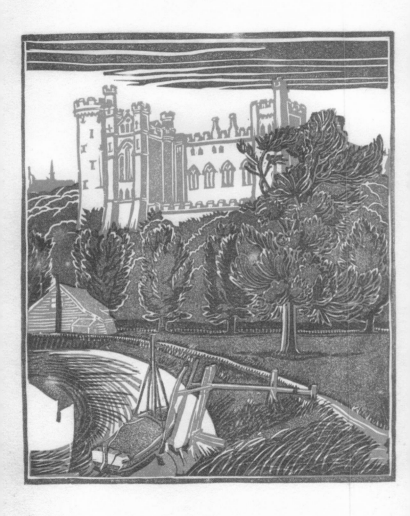

A SUSSEX ALPHABET
BY ELEANOR FARJEON

WITH ILLUSTRATIONS IN COLOUR
By Sheila M. Thompson

AT THE PEAR TREE PRESS

Arundel

Run, Arun, run and tell,
How shall men know Arundel?
A Castle Tower, a Cathedral Bell,
By these all men know Arundel.

Belloc

Mister Belloc lives in Sussex,
And don't you dare to doubt it!
He makes good cheer and drinks
    good beer,
And tells us all about it.

Chanctonbury Ring

Ring-a-ding Chanctonbury!
    What shall I sing?
Beeches on a hill-top
    All in a ring.
Green in the morning,
    Black in the night,
And burning in the autumn
    Like a beacon light.

Downs

The Downs are ups as well as downs.
Down they run to the fields and towns,
But up they go to the endless sky
Where kites and clouds and pewits fly.

Ewes

The black-nosed Southdown sheep do keep
   The Southdowns cropped as any lawn.
The grazing of the Sussex sheep
   Begins upon the Downs at dawn;
But when the evening sky grows gold
The ewes come down again to fold,
     And sleep.

9

Flint

The Caveman of Sussex he lived on the chalk,
And 'Umph! Umph! Umph!' was his manner of talk.
His tools and his weapons he fashioned of flint,
Which said as he chipped it, 'Chint! Chint! Chint!'
The Caveman of Sussex is long ago dead,
But you'll find if you're lucky his Flint Arrow-head.

Gypsy

The Gypsy peddles by Sussex day
　　And sleeps by Sussex night.
'Come, Willie, buy my lantern, pray,
　　To keep your stable bright;
And buy my clothes-pegs, Mary May,
　　Lest your pinafore blow out of sight!'

10

Harold

King Harold, King Harold, he ran out of town,
And hurried to Hastings to fight for his crown;
But an Archer let fly and King Harold fell down,
And King William the Conqueror put on his crown.

Indian Chief

As I walk Sussex, hill and shore,
I meet shepherds by the score,
Fishermen and tramps as well,
And gypsies more than I can tell.

But what I really long to meet
In country lane or village street,
And what I've never, never met,
Is an Indian Chief in Sussex yet.

Jerry's Pond

Jerry was an old man
    And lived in a Pond
With Firle at the back of him
    And Five Lords beyond.
He dined with the tadpoles,
    With newts made his bed,
And all the year round
    Had a cold in his head.

Kingcups

The floods on Amberley Wildbrooks
In Spring spread out for miles,
And the Kingcups grow in the water
Like clustering golden isles.

Long Man of Wilmington

You Long Long Man of Wilmington,
    How long have you been there?—
Before your grandsire's grandsire's grandsire's
    Grandsire's sire was seen there.

You Long Long Man of Wilmington,
    How long will you be there?—
Until your grandson's grandson's grandson's
    Grandson's son see me there.

Mushrooms

The cream-headed mushrooms
   With pinky-brown gills
They grow on the Pharisees'
   Dancing-hills.
From Bepton Down
   To Willingdon Hill
When the Pharisees dance
   You can pick your fill.

Nightingales

In Gillman's Orchard in Billingshurst
Nightingales always sing the first;
Under the apple-trees all night long
You can lie in the grass and hear their song.

And through the apple-bloom pink and white
Two or three stars will be in sight,
Like the highest, roundest, loveliest notes
Gone up to the sky from the Nightingales'
   throats.

16

Ouse

Where does River Ouse steal forth?
Near a greenwood in the North.
Where has River Ouse its mouth?
Near a haven in the South.

Pharisees

They are fairies in Norfolk,
They are fairies in Suffolk,
And fairies in Cumberland
And in Northumberland;
They are fairies in Dorset,
And fairies in Devon,
And fairies in Worcestershire,
Durham and Gloucestershire;
They are fairies in England
Where else you may please—
But in Sussex the fairies
　　　Are Pharisees.

Quarry

When along the Downs you walk
You'll find Quarries in the chalk.
Some are caves with treasure strewn,
Some are like a white half-moon,
Some are forts and kingly halls,
Some are Moorish city walls,
And one's the cliff of the world to
  me,
With tides of grass instead of sea.

Rye

Mermaid, Mermaid in the Rye,
On the hill left high and dry,
How much happier you would be
Swimming in the Winchelsea.

19

Saint Leonard's Forest

O have you seen Saint Leonard a-planting out his Forest?
Come, look up from your water-can and put your spade away!
I've searched through the trees from the Holmbush to the
    Goldings
For an old holy Forester with hair going grey—
    O have you seen Saint Leonard, Child at play?

Is he swimming in the Hammer Pond, or piping in the
        Shepherd's Field,
Or sleeping sound in Barnsnap in the heat of the day?
Is he supping in the Carter's Lodge, or sowing in the Lilybeds,
Or falling down upon his knees on Doomsday Green to pray?
    O have you seen Saint Leonard, Child at play?

But the gold-headed Child at play in Little Goldings
Looked up from his digging, laughed, and answered, 'Nay!'
And went on planting acorns and watering his beechnuts,
And the Pilgrim with his scrip and his staff went away—
    Went looking for Saint Leonard, and left the Child at play.

Tumulus

All round the Tumulus
    The four winds do blow.
Whom did they bury here
    'Twas long long ago?
Was it the Roman
    Who came as our foe
And tried to conquer Sussex,
    'Twas long long ago?
But the Downs took his heart
    Into their heart, so!
And turned it into Sussex dust,
    'Twas long long ago.

Uckfield

I went to Uckfield to swim in the sea,
But when I got there it was dry as could be.
'To Cuckfield, to Cuckfield!' a Cuckoo told me,
'For Cuckfield is Uckfield, you know, with a C.'
But Cuckfield was dry as a six-year-old pea,
So I went back to Uckfield as quick as could be.
I ducked in the grass and I dived from a tree,
And the Cuckoo of Uckfield cried 'Cuckoo' at me.

Victoria

From Victoria I can go
To Pevensey Level and Piddinghoe,
Open Winkins and Didling Hill,
Three Cups Corner and Selsey Bill.
I'm the happiest one in all the nation
When my train runs out of Victoria
  Station.

But O the day when I come to town
From Ditchling Beacon and Duncton
  Down,
Bramber Castle and Wisborough Green,
Cissbury Ring and Ovingdean!
I'm the sorriest one in all the nation
When my train runs into Victoria Station.

23

Weald

Sussex Weald is flood and field,
  Sussex Weald is wood and water.
I'll hew and drain the Sussex Weald,
  And till it for my son and daughter.

X

X is Chichester Market Cross.
If you tell me it's not, I am
  quite at a loss.

25

You

You who read this book,
  Are you Sussex born?
Do you know the look
  Of our sun at morn
And our moon at night?
  They come up Amberley crown
Like bowls of yellow light,
  Big bowls turned upside down
With all their light to spill
On table-land and hill.

You who read these rhymes,
  If you're Sussex bred,
You've seen many times
  Those bowls above your head
To golden bubbles grow
  And up the blue air swim,
Blown by some child below
  Amberley's green rim,
Some child that once you knew
Who wants to play with you.

Zouch

Lady Zouch could not keep deer
    To-day in Parham Park
If Noah had not long ago
    Kept deer inside the Ark.
I hope that Lady Zouch to-day
    Thanks Noah long ago
For every spotted fawn that runs
    With every dappled doe.

The end of A Sussex Alphabet. *The text is hand-set in* 18 *point* Perpetua *type. Printed from lino-cuts and type by* John Freeman *in* February 1939 *on* Arnold & Foster's *hand-made paper.*

Of 220 *copies, this is No.*

THE PEAR TREE PRESS
Flansham Bognor Regis
Sussex England

ALL THE WAY
TO ALFRISTON

ALL THE WAY
TO ALFRISTON
By Eleanor Farjeon

With Drawings by
ROBIN GUTHRIE

ALL THE WAY TO ALFRISTON

All the way to Alfriston,
From Chichester to Alfriston,
I went along the running Downs
High above the patchwork plain,
Fantastical as Joseph's coat
With coloured squares of grass and grain,
Earthen russets, duns and browns,
Charlock-yellow, clover-green,
Reddening wheat and silvery oat:
And rivers coiling in between,
And roofs of little peopled towns.

I heard the wind among the leaves
And corn that was not yet in sheaves
Swishing with the sound of surf;
I heard the cry of distant trains,
The rush and drip of scudding rains,
I heard my foot-beat on the turf,
The lark's delight, the pewit's plaint,
Hoarse calls of shepherds, bark and bleat,
Sheep-bells and church-bells in the heat,

And rambling thunders, far and faint:
And I saw dew-ponds round as pearls,
And multitudes of summer flowers,
Mulleins tall as little girls,
And Canterbury Bells in showers,
Fields flushed with sainfoin, banks that blazed
With golden toadflax and such fires
Of poppy that I was amazed;
And chicory as blue as heaven
Seen in clear water: I saw spires,
And thatches, castles, barns and towers,
The furnace of a clinking forge
And bridges made of wood and stone;
And by an ancient hostel even
Saw demons in the open street,
A rabbit at a Bishop's feet,
Angels and dragons and Saint George,
When I was come to Alfriston.

I ate my bread on open places,
I changed a smile with many faces,
I loved the jokes and commerce with

The jolly baker and the smith,
The gypsy with her wheedling eyes,
Her pack of wares, her pack of lies;
I loved the rain-storms and the sun,
The silent shepherds young and old,
I loved the cropping, wandering fold,
The silky dog that chased the sheep,
I loved my rest when day was done,
I loved the Downs, awake, asleep,
All the way to Alfriston,
From Chichester to Alfriston.

NOTES

NOTES

B

Hilaire Belloc (27 July 1870 – 16 July 1953), the devout Catholic, French-born poet, novelist and historian. Belloc spent his childhood in Slindon, West Sussex, and in 1906–7 purchased a house called King's Land in Shipley, West Sussex, where he and his American wife, Elodie Hogan, raised five children. His love of Sussex is reflected in several poems, most notably 'West Sussex Drinking Song' (c.1910, *Verses*), to which Farjeon is clearly alluding, and 'The South Country', a poem that was the acknowledged inspiration behind Edward Thomas' book *The South Country* (1909).

C

A prominent early Iron-Age hill fort located in West Sussex on the border between the parishes of Washington and Wiston. While evidence of Bronze Age and Roman use abounds, it is the ring of beech trees, planted by Charles Goring in 1760, that made it such a notable and mysterious site. The 1987 storm caused significant damage to the beech trees, which have since been replaced. The ring features in one of the tales in *Martin Pippin in the Apple Orchard* (1921).

D

Pronounced [pee-wit] after its alarm call, the popular name for the Northern Lapwing, *Vanellus vanellus*, a migratory flocking wader, which nests on cultivated land and in short-vegetation habitats. Once found in considerable numbers, modern farming practices have led to an 80% decline in their numbers in England and Wales since 1960 (data source, RSPB).

E

A small sheep, bred by the famous Sussex stockman John Ellman (1753–1832) of Place Farm, Glynde. This squat, robust breed produces good mutton yields and has a useable fleece.

F

A hard grey rock formed mostly of chert and found as nodule-like deposits in chalk. The South Downs are pocked with flint mines, some dating back to the Neolithic period (see J. Baczkowski, 'Learning by Experience: the Flint Mines of Southern England and Their Continental Origins', *Oxford Journal of Archaeology* (2014), 33:2, pp. 135–153. When fractured, flints were used extensively to make arrowheads and hand axes through a process of 'knapping'. Owing to their ubiquity, strength and decorative properties, they have been used extensively in Southern England for rendering and in boundary walls.

J

A small pond just off the South Downs Way in East Sussex, with the village of Firle to the north and a series of *tumuli* known as the Five Lords Burgh to the south-west. Farjeon named the lords Lionel, Hugh, Heriot, Ambrose and Hobb. Jerry's Pond was probably a 'dew pond', a man-made circular pond traditionally dug by farmers and lined with clay to provide livestock with water where other water sources were not available. The South Downs has many dew ponds owing to the porous nature of the underlying chalk, lack of hill streams, and sheep farming traditions. Despite the romantic name, most dew ponds rely on rainfall for resupply.

K

Amberley Wild Brooks is an area of wetland habitat just north of the West Sussex village of Amberley, a site of Special Scientific Interest (SSI) forming part of the River Arun flood plain. Farjeon lived in Houghton near Amberley for a brief but formative period, in a cottage in Mucky Lane. Kingcup is the local vernacular for the marsh marigold (*Caltha palustris*). The brooks are featured in *Martin Pippin in the Apple Orchard* (1921), as the place where the shepherd Young Gerard spends his holidays attempting to find the 'tallest Kingcups in the whole world'.

L

A hill figure located on the South Downs in East Sussex near the village of Wilmington. It is one of only two human hill figures in England and depicts a man holding two staffs. Previously considered Neolithic in origin, recent survey work suggests that it dates to the sixteenth or seventeenth century. In *Martin Pippin in the Daisy Field* (1937), Farjeon reuses this verse in the form of a riddle.

M

Bepton Down, near Midhurst in West Sussex, is near the most westerly stretch of the Sussex part of the South Downs. Willingdon, near Eastbourne in East Sussex, is close to the most easterly point of the South Downs.

N

The orchard featured in *Martin Pippin in the Apple Orchard* (1921), owned by Farmer Gillman who has imprisoned his daughter and has seven sirens as her jailers.

P

Sussex dialect for fairies. The Revd. W.D. Parish, in his *A Dictionary of Sussex Dialect and Collection of Provincialisms* (1875), attributes it to a phonetic variant of the 'reduplicated plural' fairieses, noting with some delight that 'the Sussex country people confuse the ideas of fairies and Pharisees in a most hopeless manner', and that 'belief in fairies is by no means extinct in the South Down districts'. Not to be confused with members of an ancient Jewish sect.

S

St. Leonard's Forest is an area of forest in the High Weald Area of Outstanding Natural Beauty, near Horsham, parts of which are claimed to be ancient forest. The Sussex Weald is rich in iron, with several phases of exploitation recorded. Significant extraction in the sixteenth and seventeenth centuries led to the creation of 'hammer' or 'furnace' ponds used to power bellows in the furnaces. The forest probably derives its name from a Frankish nobleman, St. Leonard of Limousin (c.485–559 BC), who, after founding the monastery of Noblac near Limoges, became a forest hermit. The forest also supports the myth of St. Leonard the Dragon Slayer, who slayed the last dragon in England. Injured in the encounter, at the spot where his blood fell Lily of the Valley grew, the Lilybeds to which Farjeon refers. Doomsday Green refers to one of the many clearings in the forest created by early Norman nobles granted possession shortly after the Conquest.

T

Ancient burial mound, sometimes known as a barrow.

U

Pevensey Levels, an area of marshland in East Sussex. Piddinghoe, a village in the Ouse Valley. Didling Hill, in the Rape of Chichester, West Sussex. Three Cups Corner in East Sussex is a small hamlet, so named because it is the convergence point of three watersheds. Selsey Bill, a headland town in West Sussex, the southernmost town in Sussex. 'Open Winkins' is a fictional place depicted in *Martin Pippin in the Apple Orchard* (1921). Cissbury Ring, the second largest Iron-Age hill fort in England, located approximately four miles from Worthing, West Sussex.

X

Chichester Market Cross, the finest surviving covered stone market cross in England, constructed between 1477 and 1503 by Edward Story, Bishop of Chichester.

Z

In 1922, the 17th Baroness Zouche sold Parham House, one of the country's finest Elizabethan houses, to the Hon. Clive and Alicia Pearson. In the same year 'A Sussex Alphabet' appeared in Farjeon's *Tunes of a Penny Piper*.

OXFORDSHIRE SINNERS
AND
VILLAINS

CARL BOARDMAN

OXFORDSHIRE BOOKS

ALAN SUTTON PUBLISHING LTD.

First published in the United Kingdom in 1994
Alan Sutton Publishing Limited
Phoenix Mill · Far Thrupp · Stroud · Gloucestershire
in association with Oxfordshire Books

First published in the United States of America in 1994
Alan Sutton Publishing Inc · 83 Washington Street · Dover · NH 03820

British Library Cataloguing-in-Publication Data
A catalogue record for this book is available from the British Library

ISBN 0 7509 0416 X

Library of Congress Cataloging-in-Publication Data applied for

Typeset in 11/12 Bembo.
Typesetting and origination by
Alan Sutton Publishing Limited.
Printed in Great Britain by
The Bath Press, Avon.

CONTENTS

INTRODUCTION

The origins of this book date back to 1989, the year I became County Archivist of Oxfordshire. Anxious to raise the profile of the record office, I sent out a press release proclaiming my existence, and to my horror found myself invited to be interviewed live on Radio Oxford by Phil Rapp. Dry-mouthed with terror, I turned up at the appointed time and stumbled through the interview by filling in with a couple of entertaining stories I'd picked up from the documents preserved in the record office. That, as far as I was concerned, was the beginning and end of my radio career.

A couple of weeks later, Phil rang me out of the blue. 'I liked the stories,' he said. 'How would you feel about making them a regular weekly spot?' Four years later, after featuring on Radio Four and Central TV, and a silky enquiry from a senior Oxfordshire County Council officer as to whether I work for the council and am loaned to the BBC or vice versa, the stories keep coming. Alan Sutton heard about them and suggested this book, which contains some of my favourites, roughly sorted into a life cycle. Beyond that they have little in common, except that the vast majority of them are culled from original documents, usually (though not always) held by Oxfordshire Archives, the County Council's record office, and very few of them had seen the light of day before I started broadcasting them. They're all there, together with the hundreds I haven't found yet, waiting for anyone who wants to come down and look. Whatever else your local county record office may be, it has no excuse for being boring.

A warning to scholars: do not trust this book. The sense of the quotes is always correct, as is 95 per cent of their wording, but spelling has been modernized throughout, grammar tidied up, and even on occasion tenses changed and phrases left out without the traditional (. . .), in order to make the whole thing read more smoothly. The primary purpose of this book is to entertain; those who spot something which might be of value to their more serious research would do well to check the original.

I remain grateful to Phil, who started the whole thing, and to Mary

Small, who inherited me with the early evening slot when Phil moved onward and upward. But the fact remains, I couldn't have done it alone. These days, most county archivists are so deeply involved in management that they seldom see an original document from one week to the next, and however successfully I may struggle against the stereotype, even I could not come up with a new story every week single handed. My colleagues in Oxfordshire Archives have chipped in so frequently that it is no longer possible for me to link stories with individuals; nevertheless, Liz Finn, Mark Priddey, Eleanor Roberts, Madeleine Simms, Jeanette Grisold and Robin Darwall-Smith have all contributed to this collection in one way or another, while Rosemary Hamilton has laboured to make the documents containing them actually usable. The original stories which caught Phil's attention were drawn to my attention by my predecessor, Shirley Barnes, and Sara Kinsey, Sophie Bridges and Marion Hill, all archive trainees at one time or another, contributed their share. Outside the record office, I am grateful to Eve McLaughlan, Colin Harris and Jill Valentine, who found good stories and selflessly told me about them.

Traditionally, the author ends by thanking his wife, who brought him endless cups of coffee and laid a cool hand on the fevered brow. I'm sure she must have done; more to the point, she is herself archivist to Brasenose College and the Oxfordshire Health Authority, which might explain the genesis of one or two stories in this collection, and large chunks of chapter seven are stolen verbatim from articles by her. My thanks to the Principal and Fellows of the King's Hall and College of Brasenose, and to the Health Authority, for allowing me to use those stories, but even greater thanks to Liz for finding them, encouraging me, giving me the benefit of professional as well as personal judgement, and generally being around. She has also done far more than her share of the washing up over the past few weeks.

Oxford
August 1993

CHAPTER ONE

FATHER TO THE MAN

Good sinners and villains are hard to find. Most are petty individuals, untutored, incompetent types, who constantly get it wrong and provide an endless source of entertainment for their more law-abiding brethren: poisoners who can't persuade anyone to drink their highly suspicious potions, forgers who haven't quite grasped that people have widely differing styles of handwriting, drunken clergymen who fail to spot those occasions on which they ought to be wearing trousers. For every genuinely ruthless villain there are half a dozen sinners who are more endearing than repulsive; one would almost be inclined to invite John Martin, the seventeenth-century rector of Begbroke, round for dinner, were it not for the fact that you could never afford to restock the drinks cabinet.

How do they turn out this way? Is it the result of childhood trauma, a deprived upbringing, being born to the wrong parents, brought up in the wrong home environment or in the wrong century – assuming they could lay claim to more than one parent and a home environment that wasn't more accurately characterized as a roadside ditch? For a lot of Oxfordshire children over the centuries, their first glimpse of the great outside world must have given them a shrewd idea that life was not going to be a bed of roses or, come to that, very long.

One of the major problems facing any child of poor parents was the pre-1834 Poor Law, with particular reference to the rules on settlement. Reduced to their simplest form, these laid down the ways in which an individual could become the responsibility of a particular parish, whose ratepayers would then be forced to provide the necessary cash to support him or her when poverty struck. The easiest way of gaining a settlement in a parish was to be born there, and many honest, upstanding ratepayers went to considerable lengths to ensure that this occurred as infrequently as possible. The merest rumour of a pregnant pauper within the parish boundaries was enough to have respectable householders on the streets, prepared to repel all boarders.

Plot, in his *Natural History of Oxfordshire*, refers to the story of the elm tree of Bletchingdon. A 'poor, great bellyed woman' had arrived in the village in the last stage of pregnancy, only to find the doors of all the houses, not to mention the Angel and Crown Inn, shut against her, in the pious hope that she would make it to the next parish before going into labour. In fact she reached the village green, where there stood a huge elm tree with a hollow trunk, into which she climbed for shelter and where she gave birth to a son. As it happened they needn't have bothered; the son grew into 'a lusty young man', went to live near Harwich, and never bothered them again – for which they had cause to be quite thankful.

By contrast, the unnamed son of Elizabeth Johnson, a widow of Londonderry, caused the parish authorities of Nettlebed, Nuffield and Ewelme considerable trouble. On 6 December 1727 Elizabeth 'came to the parish of Nettlebed to the house of one Jones, with her male child about five years old, and then and there she agreed with the said Jones for lodging at two pence a night, and she lodged there two nights and paid for her lodging four pence'. This perfectly conventional financial agreement abruptly went sour on Monday morning when Mrs Jones realized that the boy was ill. With a shrewd idea who was going to end up paying for treatment and support, she ordered the mother to get the child out of the place at once. Elizabeth Johnson refused. Mrs Jones hadn't prospered in the lodgings trade by letting moral scruples get in the way of sound business practice; she 'took the child by force out of the bed and carried it into the parish of Nuffield, and there delivered it to another woman in her company, who laid the child down in Nuffield near the Crown Alehouse and went their way'.

Thus it was that William Hussey, keeper of the Crown ale house, Nuffield, had his Monday morning completely ruined by finding a sick pauper child in the snow on his doorstep. With the same finely tuned sense of priorities between humanitarian principles and financial greed which evidently motivated Elizabeth Jones, he lost no time in trying to get the boy out of the parish and off his rates bill. He ran for Edward Fenell, the churchwarden, but the two of them apparently decided not to dirty their own hands with the deed; instead they brought in a local villager called John Arthur who, in the mother's words, 'by force and violence, the child being sick and not able to travel, did bring the child into the parish of Ewelme, and laid it down in the street under a wall belonging to Thomas Scot of Ewelme, the ground being then covered with snow'.

Presumably Ewelme was a less ruthless parish, as no complaint was laid against the authorities or inhabitants there. But Elizabeth Johnson called the various individuals who had persecuted her in Nettlebed and Nuffield before the magistrates at Quarter Sessions, where John Arthur for one made the time-honoured excuse that he was only obeying orders, and that the orders were misleading anyway: 'Edward Fenell said that I be kind to help the child forward . . . I set it down near the church rails; the child then being not able to stand I held it up till his mother received it. . . .' It seems that Fenell was a little vague about the object of Arthur's kindness, though if Arthur thought it was kind to drag a child who couldn't stand through the snow, he must have been startlingly naïve. There is no record of judgement being passed against the defendants; what they did was unusually heartless, but it wasn't illegal.

At no point is the child's father mentioned, and it would hardly be surprising if he was unknown. Another stipulation of the law was that men were responsible for the support of their bastard children, financially embarrassing at the best of times, and embarrassing in quite another way if they happened to be married to someone other than the mother. Denying everything was not always enough; small village communities tended to know just about everything there was to know about the sex lives of their members and, as will be amply demonstrated in the next chapter, any charge of sexual misdemeanours found witnesses crawling out of the woodwork who had apparently been sitting by the bedside taking notes. It was far more astute to find a fall guy.

In this respect the good old chestnut about the son of the household having his way with the innocent maidservant still had a lot of mileage in it. Thomas Stocker of Iffley used it before he had even laid a hand on the girl in question: 'he sollicited Mistress Alice Smith, maid, of Iffley, to lay with him, and told her if she proved with child she might lay the child to her young master'. Just in case she had any moral scruples on the matter, Stocker pointed to the example of her betters: 'he farther said that one Swiftin and her mistress were often caught together, and bad her watch them, and she would see it as well as he had done'. None of this did him the slightest good in the long run, since the quotations above come from the evidence in the 1672 paternity suit against him.

Over in Standlake, the young masters were obviously getting wise to this trick, and one of them decided to turn the tables. In April 1693 Christopher Savage, a labourer, took his master Henry Hughes before Edmund Warcupp, Justice of the Peace, for refusing to pay him or give him his food rations, 'at which time the said Henry Hughes did confess and own that he had been in bed with Elizabeth Thorne, his maidservant'. At first sight this appears to be rather an odd subject to bring up for discussion in the circumstances, but all is revealed as Warcupp's examination continues. Henry Hughes was the son of Thomas Hughes, who kept Christopher Savage and Elizabeth Thorne as live-in servants. As was not unusual in small households, Henry and Christopher shared a bed, but what was a little more out of the ordinary, Elizabeth Thorne was apparently in the habit of coming round to tuck them in for the night.

One evening, 'the said Elizabeth coming to tuck up the clothes, Henry Hughes bid Christopher Savage pull her to bed, which he did, and immediately she went into the middle of the bed, being then in her smock which, Savage seeing, he immediately rose and went away', which suited Henry very well indeed. Where Savage spent the night we never learn, but we do know that 'Henry and Elizabeth lay all that night together', with consequences which might have been expected. When Savage returned the following morning, Henry told him something to his disadvantage: 'that Elizabeth would lay her bastard child to him [Christopher Savage] as he would wager, and not unto him the said Hughes, because he should be married ere long'.

He wasn't the only one, because Henry had a devious plan. He wanted Savage to marry Elizabeth and then desert her; this would give the child an official father, but because that father could not be found 'the parish might keep the child, and Henry Hughes might escape the shame of the bastard'. Everyone wins except the ratepayers of the parish, and of course Elizabeth who doesn't count, but Savage could hardly be expected to do this out of the kindness of his heart. He was bribed: 'Hughes said he would give him twenty pounds, and likewise desired Elizabeth to marry Christopher Savage with the like promise of twenty pounds'. £40 was a lot of money, but Savage obviously didn't fancy Henry's cast-offs, and when he went away to visit friends at Kidlington, he didn't come back. Henry, one of life's optimists who could see the silver lining in every cloud, 'told Elizabeth that if he did not return to his service, he would give her some part of the wages which were at that time due to him, and the rest they would make merry withall'.

Elizabeth went off to her family at Burford for her confinement, and during her absence there was a *rapprochement* of sorts between Hughes and Savage; the latter turned up on her doorstep one day 'and prevailed with her to return to Standlake, since which time they have lived together in one house [which they rented] at bed and board, but she denies that she was ever married to him'. The reason for this was that: 'he doth refuse to marry her for want of the twenty pounds promised'. In failing to pay his bribes Henry had failed to observe the cardinal rule of the successful crook, and so found himself before Justice Warcupp, formally accused of failing to pay Savage's wages and keep, but obviously being pestered for the promised loot. It never came, and Christopher and Elizabeth failed to live happily ever after; her final word on the subject is that 'on Tuesday last he ran away from her, she knows not whither'. But to the end he proved himself of a stronger moral calibre than his master, for 'he told her before he departed that if she was with child by him since their cohabitation he would return to her and marry her and labour to maintain her'.

Where Stocker and Hughes went wrong was in fixing on another local individual to blame for an unwanted child, since that individual could always turn awkward and object. There were two obvious alternatives, and in 1690 Jeffrey Smith of Blackthorne tried both of them. At the beginning of 1691 a certain Jane Peisley was delivered of a bastard child, and not unnaturally the parish authorities were very interested in the name of the father. Nor did they have much compunction about how they got it; although torturing pregnant women was generally considered to be beyond the pale, a fairly similar result could be obtained by simple non-intervention during her labour pains. She was cross-examined by the midwife and other women 'in the time of her extreme pains and delivery' and rapidly came up with Jeffrey Smith's name. Subsequently she came up with a good deal more.

Smith was a married man, and thus had more to worry about even than the considerable costs of maintaining a bastard during its formative years. The moment he realized that Jane was pregnant, he knew he had to take immediate action; the precise action he took was to turn up on her doorstep with 'several medicines to procure abortion, to make her miscarry, charging her to take the same, and telling her that they would do the feat, and advising her to other outward applications to effect the same ill design'. Jane may have been stupid enough to sleep with him, but not so much as to drink the contents of the bottles on his say; it could hardly fail to occur to her that his ends would be equally well served by an induced abortion or by her being carried out of her house in a box. 'Which medicines the said Jane Peisley being afraid to take', as she succinctly put it, Smith came round to see how matters were progressing, and 'for fear of displeasing him Jane Peisley did make answer that she had taken the medicines but found they would not do'. He must have been expecting a rather more spectacular result, as 'with many repeated oaths he did swear that she had not taken the medicines, for if she had he knew they would have done the trick'.

The first ploy having failed, Smith fell back on his second line of defence. He needed a plausible alternative father for the forthcoming child, and with a largeness of vision which had eluded Stocker and Hughes he saw that a fictitious figure would be far easier to manipulate than a real one. What he needed was a husband for Jane, a mysterious figure with an untraceable name – say, Joseph Johnson – who was a travelling man, had come from nowhere, married her, fathered the child, and vanished again into oblivion. Nobody from nowhere has always had a facility for escaping from difficult situations. The only problem here was that some proof of this unlikely marriage would be called for, specifically a solidly attested entry in a church marriage register. The basic requirement in such a situation was a corrupt clergyman. Fortunately he had one to hand.

Thomas Heydon was rector of nearby Cottisford. He was also one of the victims of the drop in real terms of many clerical incomes. To make ends meet he was prepared to connive at a great deal, and back in 1683 he had found himself before the ecclesiastical courts for marrying three couples without banns or licences. Now he seemed perfect for Jeffrey Smith's purposes, particularly as time was getting short. On Christmas Eve 1690 Smith sent him a Christmas present, in the form of Henry Wood, a labourer from Ambrosden, bearing hard cash. Wood's job was to obtain a fake marriage certificate, to which end Smith gave him 'twenty shillings for procuring the certificate and one shilling for his day's work, promising him a greater reward if he succeeded in it'. Two days later, having been involved in some astute financial calculations in the interim, Wood arrived at the rectory and put the proposition to its inhabitant, 'which at first Thomas Heydon was unwilling to grant, saying he durst not do it, but when Henry Wood had told him he brought money to pay him and had laid down four half crowns [otherwise known as 10s., which shows how profitable a couple of days' financial calculation can be] in his window for his reward, then Thomas Heydon did in the presence of Henry Wood write a certificate in such manner as was desired'.

Smith took the certificate to Jane Peisley, 'telling her that he had now done what all the devils in hell could not undo and gained her the certificate, charging her to stand to it and swear that she had not been in his company for two years'. It was a brave try, but unfortunately it reckoned without the persuasive talents of the parish authorities and their midwives. Smith's big mistake was to use Heydon for the certificate. If he knew Heydon was bribeable, so did the Church authorities. Since 1683 the rector had been a marked man, and his ecclesiastical superiors were watching him like hawks. The sight of his signature on a document of any description was enough to have it called into question, and this one already read like a fairy story. The parish closed in on Jane Peisley, who had enough problems without trying to protect a man she suspected of trying to poison her.

When news was brought to him that Jane had talked, Smith was terribly

Dr Robert Plot, antiquarian, professor of chemistry, and expert on trees and Woodstock devils (*Oxfordshire Archives*)

Room to swing a cat? The baptistry of St Mary's Henley, where Tom received his name (*Centre for Oxfordshire Studies*)

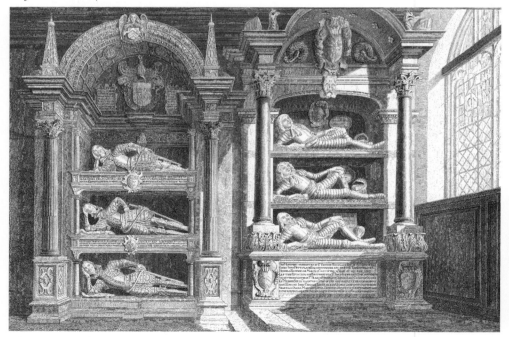

John Fettiplace, founder of Swinbrook School, reclining in the company of his ancestors (*Centre for Oxfordshire Studies*)

annoyed and he 'cursed Jane Peisley for a fool', crying that 'the jade was faint hearted, and if she had stood to it all the devils in hell could not have hurt her'. Generally speaking, Smith seems to have been very well informed on the character and abilities of all the devils in hell; maybe he was prescient. On this occasion he was one more failure in an endless series of attempts to bamboozle the parish authorities, and he paid for it in various types of coin. Meanwhile, in the background, the unfortunate Thomas Heydon was hauled off once more to stand trial before his bishop.

Once a child was in the world, the immediate priority was to baptize it, lest it die suddenly and go to hell. The parish registers of England are full of males with female names and vice versa, the legacy of drunken or careless midwives who couldn't be bothered to check closely on what they had just delivered. On the other hand they could usually be certain that, male or female, it was at least human. The collections of the Oxford antiquary Hearne do mention the case of Mary Toft of Godalmin, who in 1726 claimed to have given birth to seventeen rabbits, but it is only fair to add that the Court of King's Bench did not believe her. Yet not everything baptized in the local parish church walked on two legs, particularly if the bellringers of Henley-on-Thames had anything to do with it.

On 23 November 1662 they turned up for ringing at the church as usual in the evening, but a certain Isaac Keene brought a cat with him 'and made him soft in the church till they had rung the eight o'clock bell; and after the bell was rung they carried the cat to the font and one of them taking up the cover of the font, Benjamin Wooldridge took out water out of the font and sprinkled the cat, which Thomas Talent had in his arms, and named the cat Tom [what else?] and appointed Isaac Keene and Thomas Wheeler to be the gossips [godparents]'. The inhabitants of seventeenth-century Henley were easily amused, but the Church was far less inclined to take a joke. Indeed, it started to use words such as 'blasphemy', which was enough to chill the blood in any seventeenth-century veins. The accused were forced to grovel before the ecclesiastical courts, pleading that 'they did not use the words christen or baptize, but did this out of indiscreet wantonness, and not out of intention to deprave the holy sacrament of baptism'.

Of course, the Church was bound to be a little touchy in the aftermath of the Cromwellian interregnum, and the bellringers had used the font of St Mary's, possibly the disused one which still stands in the church. In Chipping Norton the same response to a similar event seems harsher, perhaps because the Church itself was not involved. John Risson gave evidence that 'on a Sabbath day in August last, he being in the house of John Higgins the elder, together with Higgins, John Garrick, John Brown, John Walter and John Reeve were drinking and eating peas, and would suffer none to eat with them unless his name were John, and some coming unto them whose names were not John, they undertook to name them John, sprinkling or throwing drink in their faces, and so named them John, and then suffered them to eat peas with them'. A silly joke based on a minor coincidence over Christian names was not calculated to appeal to the local clergy; once again the accused were obliged to deny the use of the word baptism or any words of the sacrament, and did not escape without a fine.

Still, the majority of individuals baptized in Oxfordshire were children, and assuming they didn't actually starve or fall prey to one of the less pleasant diseases going the rounds, the first few years of their lives were likely to be as uneventful as any. Their problems really began when they were old enough to go to school.

Before 1870 their chances of getting to school at all were fairly remote. The earliest attempts to bring education to the children of the labouring poor were generally sponsored by the Nonconformists; they had the wit to recognize the propaganda advantages of getting their subjects young. The Church of England was surprisingly slow on the uptake here, and even when the upper echelons of the Church saw the point, they sometimes had terrible difficulty explaining it to the priest in the parish. In 1815 the Bishop of Oxford sent a questionnaire to all his clergy asking about the state of education in their parishes, with particular reference to the use of the National Society's monitorial system. The incumbent of Rotherfield Peppard was typical of many who replied:

> I conceive Peppard to be a very central spot for the establishment of a National School, there being many hamlets in the neighbourhood placed at a very inconvenient distance from their respective parish churches. . . . Such an establishment, I am convinced, would rescue a number of children from the grasp of the Methodists, who are very indefatigable. And the desire the labouring poor have to give their childen a little schooling is inconceivable. . . .

The inability to understand that the poor might want to give their children a decent start in life through education was widespread, and sometimes linked to the rather less naïve belief that they should at all costs be prevented from doing so. Vaughan Thomas, the nineteenth-century rector of Yarnton, was a public benefactor, a pioneer in public health and the treatment of the insane, a man lavish with his time and his private purse, and not at all eager to see the working man rise above his station. In 1818 he wrote:

I have established and now for twelve years continued a day and Sunday school upon such a plan as I see and know to be the best adapted to the course of service in a small agricultural parish, such as is suitable to the well-known relations of the children, to their state and condition, their labours and interests in my parish. I find the poor willing enough to have their children taught but in the establishment of this school I have done my best to adapt everything to the social relations of our poor children in Yarnton, to their prospects (as intended for labours manual), to the purposes of the yeomanry who employ them, and though last yet principally to make them good Christians.

I deprecate all parliamentary and legislative regulation for a universal system of parochial instruction. It is not in the power of Parliament to devise any one plan that shall be suitable for all the poor children of the kingdom, for what may be suitable and sufficient for some of them will not be so for others. Those that live in manufacturing or maritime districts, where there are various employments for the poor in some commercial way, require another sort of civil instruction from those who have no chance of getting into such situations. It will be worse than folly to make a peasant's boy who can earn three shillings or four shillings [15p or 20p] a week at ten years old, stay at school to be taught what he can never turn to account in his own parish, but which, when learned, will make him desirous of roaming in order to find a place where he may make his talent useful. That this is the effect produced by educating poor children above their obvious and acknowledged interests is evident from the fact that no children of the poor are better educated than the Scotch, and none migrate so numerously or so far.

A clearer statement of the blinkered belief that education is or should be no more than vocational training, a means of providing fuel for the country's economic machine, would be hard to find. It was to be some time before the civilized notion of education to develop human beings as individuals gained a firm foothold, and even now that foothold may not be as firm as we think.

Of course, those children from the social orders where an education was a realistic expectation might well regret the fact. As elsewhere, the sixteenth and seventeenth centuries saw the foundation of several grammar schools in Oxfordshire, each with its set of statutes to illustrate what might be expected of such an institution. In about 1652 John Fettiplace founded Swinbrook School, and was no exception. Just to make sure that the schoolmaster didn't get any ideas of his own on the running of the establishment, he laid down that should such a man fail to keep the statutes and refuse to do the decent thing – i.e. resign – he was to forfeit £40. He was to be a BA of Oxford at least, be of sound religion and walk before his scholars in all sobriety and decent conversation as a pattern of godliness and morality. This paragon of virtue was not to hold a curacy unless it was a sinecure, that is one in which he did no work but got the money, which may seem somewhat contradictory to us, but the definition of morally acceptable conduct has changed a little over the years.

Then the statutes get to work on the boys. Scholars were not to be beaten on the head or pulled by the ears, nose, cheek or hair. This sounds very reasonable, until one starts to consider why it was necessary to write such stipulations into the statutes – simply because it would scarcely have occurred to the average schoolmaster to maintain discipline in any other way. Leave to play was not to be allowed more than one afternoon a week. Even Fettiplace had to face the problem of the distinguished old boy who returns to the school, gives a rousing speech to the pupils, and concludes his address by calling on the headmaster to grant a half day's holiday, but unlike many others Fettiplace had a way of dealing with it: if two holidays were allowed in one week at the request of some man of special worth or love, then no holiday was to be allowed at all the following week. School hours were to be ten hours in summer and eight in winter. Boys were to speak in Latin and refrain from childish jangling and loud speaking. There are shades here of King Edward VI School in Stourbridge, where boys were also to refrain from filthy talk, which speaks volumes for their fluency in Latin.

The uneducated poor and the classically educated rich: the future impoverished labourers and the future landowners, magistrates and rulers. It would be so convenient and tidy if one could point to the one environment as producing the sinners and villains, the other producing men of integrity and righteousness. Of course life just isn't like that, and if there is a distinction between the two groups it can only be that the educated tend to be devious with it. And both groups started to show their true colours once they had passed adolescence and sex started to rear its far from ugly head.

CHAPTER TWO

SEX AND MARRIAGE

If the extent to which a society is sexually obsessed can be gauged by the common currency of its insults and imprecations, very little has changed in the past few hundred years. Walking through London or central Oxford in the evening, the casual passer-by has ample opportunity to reflect on the paucity of vocabulary employed in obscene insults and the staggering inarticulacy of its users. When, in 1690 Joseph Twicross yelled at Sara Colton, 'You are a bitch, you are a fat-arsed whore, you are a greasy-arsed whore, huswife, you are a whore, I know you to be a whore and you know I know you to be a whore, you are an old bawd, you keep a couple of whores in the house, one for your husband and another for your son!', he was at least making up in vigour what he lacked in subtlety. And if his vocabulary seems none too extensive, bear in mind that he was levelling a quite explicit accusation at Mrs Colton, rather than just intimating to her that she was not among his favourite neighbours.

Similarly, when Richard Wiggins of Witney told William Fairbrother that he saw a man lie with his wife twice in five minutes and that it was not the first, second or third time, he was not simply trying to annoy the unfortunate Mr Fairbrother, although doubtless he managed to do so. If we assume that he wasn't complimenting Mrs Fairbrother on her sexual agility and dispatch either, and that there is a slight exaggeration in the timespan quoted, Wiggins was quite serious, either in believing that Hannah Fairbrother engaged in regular adultery or prostitution, or, more to the point, in wishing everyone else to believe it; so much so that Hannah's reputation was seriously compromised, and she took Wiggins to the bishop's court for slander.

This story underlines two points about English society in the period between about 1500 and 1800. The first is that the modern concept of privacy was largely unknown. Neighbours lived close together in tightly knit, at times literally incestuous communities, and the amount of detail they knew about one another's most intimate lives and habits was quite astonishing; from the point of view of the modern social historian, it is also extremely useful. From the point of view of contemporaries it was ruinous, as an individual's reputation and standing in the community could be destroyed very easily, which brings us to the second point: there was a form of remedy which does not exist today. The court of the local bishop existed to deal not only with cases in which religious faith was directly involved, but also with those relating to morals, be it outrageous sexual conduct or the slander which imputed it. Since moral offences were considered to be an extremely serious matter, so accusations of them took on an equal gravity, and there was no such thing as a casual insult which impugned someone's morality. The judgement of the court, quite apart from the penance it might inflict, could seal the defendant's fate within his local society.

Nowhere is this more clearly seen than in courtship, marriage and the various stages of breakdown leading to divorce – insofar as such an outcome was possible before the nineteenth century. Not all marriages were contracted in the manner of the Standlake trio; there were plenty of honest and above-board betrothals, even where the marriage bed had been anticipated. It was simply that some fiancés were slipperier than others.

John Jorden was particularly adept at oiling his way out of difficult situations. Jorden lived in the vicarage house in Bampton (for no readily apparent reason, since he wasn't the vicar) and this gave him ample opportunity to see Hester Jones of that town. Before long certain rumours began to find their way about the parish, and eventually reached the ears of Thomas Jones, Hester's brother. Learning that (a) his sister was pregnant, but that (b) Jorden had accepted responsibility and was prepared to marry her, Thomas went for a stroll across to the vicarage. Jorden was out, but Thomas assured them that he was prepared to wait. Eventually his quarry returned to discover that perennial nightmare of seducers, the girl's brother waiting for him in his own living-room; he can hardly have been reassured by Thomas following the time-honoured tradition and 'desiring him that he might talk a few words with him in the garden'. Doubtless to his relief, this turned out for once not to be an invitation to step outside and be beaten to a pulp. Thomas really did want to talk, and he spoke as follows: 'John, it doth appear by my brother's report that my sister Hester Jones is with child, and she herself doth acknowledge it, and it appears both by her speeches and by your own confession, as I hear, that she was begotten with child by you.'

This refreshingly low-key attitude gave Jorden the chance to start talking himself out of the situation. He had kept Hester quiet with promises of marriage for as long as could reasonably be expected; now he moved on to her family. He said it was all true and that he did intend to make her his wife, whereupon Thomas pressed him: 'When will you marry her? She is near her time of delivery of child, and therefore it were good it were dispatched for both your credits.' Jorden 'replied and said she was with child by him, and swore that he would marry her and make her his wife, and would have no other to be his wife but only her, but said he could not name the time when he would marry her, and entreated Thomas very earnestly not to importune him to his reasons wherefore he would defer his marrying her' – promise them anything, but always leave an escape clause.

Jorden evidently thought he could continue to amuse himself with Hester while keeping the rest of the family on a string. What he hadn't counted on was Thomas' ability to pop up out of the woodwork every time he was getting down to business with the girl, asking awkward questions. On the Thursday of Whitsun week 1629 he got Hester into the buttery in her house, when Thomas suddenly loomed up 'urging John Jorden to marry her the said Hester'. Jorden 'swore as God should save him he would marry Hester and make her his wife' and that he was only delaying 'for some private reasons known to himself'. Thomas was getting a little fed up with these mysterious private reasons; now that he had Jorden trapped in his own buttery, he wanted some straight answers.

'John, my sister has but a small marriage portion. Is that the cause?' he asked. 'No,' said Jorden, 'I care nothing for the money.' 'Well then, do you suspect that she has been dishonest with any other?' pursued Thomas. No, no, as God should save him he thought she had not been dishonest with any but himself. Had he then engaged himself to any other woman? Jorden fervently denied it, and finally managed to get out of the house by offering to take Hester to the town cross and there proclaim her to be his wife, which had one great advantage over a church wedding in that it wasn't legally binding. The Jones household was becoming a dangerous place to visit.

Indeed Bampton was becoming a little too hot to hold him, and a few days later we find John Jorden in the Cross Inn, near the market house in Oxford, drowning his sorrows in ale. Court proceedings seldom go into psychological detail, so we are denied the thoughts which went through his mind when he looked up and saw a familiar figure standing by his table. Thomas, on the other hand, was delighted to see his old acquaintance. Oxford was the seat of the diocese and the archdeaconry, and therefore the appropriate place to take out a marriage licence. 'If you intend to marry my sister,' he pointed out, 'you should do well while you are in town to take one out, and then you might be married when you will, and that would stay the speeches of people and prevent further trouble.' He did not go into any detail as to the trouble which might be expected if Jorden failed to take out a licence, but the point seems to have been made. The seducer waxed almost lyrical on the advantages and desirability of his heading over to the bishop's official at once and acquiring a licence from him. In fact he was so carried away with the idea that on leaving the inn he completely forgot to do anything about it.

Thomas' patience was exhausted, as indeed was the term of his sister's pregnancy. When she gave birth he took out a breach of promise suit against Jorden, which he had no difficulty in winning, as half the inhabitants of Bampton seem to have known about the promise to marry Hester. In the twentieth century the whole idea of breach of promise seems like a rather hollow form of revenge for bruised emotions, but for someone like Hester it could at least do something towards restoring her reputation and the honour of her family. What finally brought the action into disrepute was the sort of woman who made a living at it – someone like Mary Nicholls.

Mary Nicholls was active in St Cross parish, Oxford, around 1670, to the regret of a certain John Dew. She claimed that Dew had promised to marry her, and swore that if he did not she would sue him for breach of promise, unless, of course, he chose to offer a settlement out of court. 'She, the said Mary Nicholls, publicly reported and boasted that she was to marry John Dew upon May Day by four of the clock in the morning or not at all, and that she would have him to be her husband, or if she had him not she would get five pounds out of him.' Already the whole business begins to sound like a put-up job; in common with so many incompetent sinners and villains, Mary had failed to grasp that one vital factor in any plan to swindle someone is not telling everyone about it. Had she played the unfortunate, jilted girl she might have stood a chance. Unfortunately, 'she said that if she could get five pounds out of him she did not care whether she had him or no' and 'further boasted, reported and said that she did not give a pin whether she married John Dew or no, but if John would not marry her she would get half his estate, and she was sure that the law would give it her'. Even such blatant evidence of gold-digging would not excuse Dew if he genuinely had abandoned her; however, Mary had made the even more elementary mistake of not setting up her witnesses before boasting of her plan. She went to one Bernard Woods and 'in order to execute and effect her malicious design told him that if he would witness for her she would give him full satisfaction if she could get anything out of John Dew'. Bernard went and told the court, and another inept money-making scheme bit the dust.

One simply had to be very careful with whom one contracted marriage around Oxford in the seventeenth and eighteenth centuries. Some people were completely untrustworthy. One 'bold, wild' individual (according to the antiquary Hearne), the offspring of an apothecary at Carfax, made a practice of strolling about Oxfordshire and the neighbouring counties, courting any women who were available and marrying them. The only reason this particular individual avoided a swingeing prosecution under the bigamy laws was that the marriages were not legal in the first place. The multiple bridegroom was, in fact, the apothecary's daughter, who liked to put on men's clothing and act the part; eventually she was locked up at Worcester, being described as 'somewhat delirious' which led her to 'commit these unaccountable pranks'. In the twentieth century we might discern a far more rational impulse behind her activities.

One way of being absolutely certain of what you were getting in the sex and marriage stakes was to keep it within the family. The problem with this was that the authorities had a distinct bias against incest, and it was necessary to keep very quiet about it. This was not easy when every parish in the country seems to have been full of keen amateur detectives. William Piggott and Elizabeth Whatton, reputed brother and sister in Stanton St John in the year 1610, tried to be discreet about it, but were foiled by the terrible quality of building work in that neck of the woods. Draper, the next door neighbour, claimed he had no option but to become an unwilling spectator of their activities:

> About Easter last, looking into the house of John Whatton in Madcroft in the parish of Stanton about five or six o'clock in the morning, I saw William Piggott and Elizabeth Whatton lying together in bed naked, saving he had his shirt and she a smock, and so has seen them divers mornings together, there being but a mud wall between my chamber and the chamber of John Whatton, which wall was broken down so much that a man might easily pass through. . . .

His wife Mary confirmed the story: 'I did see them naked in bed together in such sort as men and women go to bed, in the chamber of John Whatton, and they were in bed together alone, nobody being in the room with them.' One is left wondering why, if the Drapers were so scandalized by this, they spent divers mornings watching it before going to the authorities.

Frequently it was left to those of the clergy who were more understanding or more immoral, depending on your point of view, to tidy up the tangled sex lives of their parishioners with a well-timed wedding, even if that wedding was strictly against the rules. John Allen Giles, the nineteenth-century curate of Bampton, was particularly active in this field. He was no stranger to clashes with his diocesan superiors. Chiefly remembered now for a history of Bampton which he himself was fond of denigrating but which has survived far better than most of its date, his publishing activities were quite extensive. Using a private printing press which he kept in the parish vicarage, he produced a number of pamphlets expounding his personal, highly idiosyncratic theological views, which so offended the Bishop of Oxford that a ban was finally placed on a number of projected works on the grounds that they were contrary to the doctrines of the Anglican Church. This gave Giles the free time to offend his bishop even more drastically by his cavalier attitude towards the laws governing marriages in the Church of England.

Giles was indicted in 1854 for marrying Richard Pratt and Jane Green at Bampton without banns or a licence and before 8 a.m. It was fairly obvious that such a hasty and surreptitious marriage must have had a reason. Pratt was an apprentice, and his master, James Butler, cryptically remarked 'that if this job had not happened, something worse would'. A letter from J.M. Davenport, Clerk of the Peace, to the Bishop of Oxford expanded on this remark: 'Evidence will be given that Dr Giles knew that the girl was in the family way. This supplies a motive for the irregular marriage.'

Davenport and the bishop – none other than the famous 'Soapy Sam' Wilberforce, a shrewd operator whom we shall meet again in the course of this book – had to tread a very careful path in the prosecution. The Clerk of the Peace wrote in a private letter:

> Dr Giles' solicitor will endeavour to quote anything which falls or has fallen from your Lordship. It will be endeavoured to elicit that your Lordship either is, or is not, the prosecutor. It is important that we should be agreed upon it, because I expect them to cross-examine me upon the subject. I shall state then that representations in the way of grave complaint having been made to your Lordship respecting the marriage of Pratt and Green in uncanonical hours, and without banns or licence, you desired me to investigate it, and that having done so, and finding the scandal it had caused in the neighbourhood, and that the real facts were denied by Dr Giles, your Lordship desired that information should be given before a civil magistrate, treating the offence as a statutory one. . . .

The implication seems to have been that a measure of popular sympathy was behind Giles, and the bishop had to be seen to have been forced to take action due to local complaints, and to have had no choice but to hand the matter over to the civil arm.

In fact, the prosecution need not have worried; everyone connected with the affair lined up to testify against the unfortunate Giles. Thomas Plaster, the parish clerk of Bampton, not only testified to the fatal entry in the marriage register being in the curate's handwriting, but further added that Giles had taken the church keys very early in the morning with no very good explanation. Charlotte Lait, the supposed witness to the marriage according to the register, positively denied being there. All that was needed was for the couple themselves to come forward, but when the prosecution searched for them they met their first obstacle. A certain Mr Roberts of Islington, an old friend of Giles', had bought them off in the most effective way possible by paying for them to emigrate to Australia, from where even the most zealous prosecutor was not going to recall them. It would be pleasant to think that such a masterstroke was rewarded with success, but the weight of evidence from those who had no wish to travel and see the world was quite enough to condemn the defendant. Giles was found guilty and sentenced to a year's imprisonment in Oxford gaol. He was, however, released on 3 June 1855 after serving only three months of his sentence, thanks to the intervention of the bishop and several gentlemen and clergy. It appears, therefore, that Wilberforce merely wanted to teach him a lesson.

Of course there could be perfectly legal marriages which caused even more of a furore than the Giles affair. The unfortunate problem of Black Moll, which taxed the ingenuity of the churchwardens and overseers of the parish of St Peter in the East, Oxford, in 1697, was such a case. Black Moll was the local prostitute, which was a minor headache for the St Peter's authorities in that she occasionally came to them for poor relief and put the local rates up. More regrettably she was a careless prostitute, and managed to get herself pregnant. This was much more serious, as both she and her bastard child were going to end up as a long-term charge on the parish, which was really adding insult to injury. The only way of getting the woman and her future progeny off their hands was to marry her off to someone in another parish, which would then take on the responsibility for her – if such a person could be found.

Enter one Henry Hopkins, apothecary of St Peter's parish, the authorities' fixer; his mission: to find a compliant idiot who would get Black Moll out of Oxford. The one he found was Thomas Pether of Cowley, 'aged near 70 years, and one who of a long time has obtained and still doth receive weekly alms there', who was soon seduced by the promise of a comely young wench, and was 'wheedled to lodge in the parish of St Peter's at the house of one Edward Musgrave, a victualler'. The parish authorities left nothing to chance; they provided a marriage licence, a parson, a wedding ring and 'whatever else might be requisite for the accomplishing of the design', namely the unloading of Black Moll on the Cowley parish rates bill. All was in readiness, and on Whitsunday morning Thomas Pether woke up eager for his wedding day. At this point, however, things suddenly began to move very quickly.

The churchwardens and overseers of Cowley had been tipped off at the last minute. As Pether prepared to meet his bride-to-be, they burst into Musgrave's house and informed him that he was going nowhere except back to Cowley, and he certainly wasn't marrying any loose woman from St Peter's. Unfortunately, just as they were explaining this to him they were ambushed by the St Peter's churchwardens, and that was when the fight began.

According to the Cowley contingent, 'the churchwardens and overseers of St Peter's rushed in upon them, snatched away the Constable of Cowley's hat from off his head and flung it out of the room, tore the hair off his head with great force and violence, withall using foul and reproachful language and bitterly inveighing against all of them, and threatened further violence towards them, even to the beating their very heads off'. The St Peter's mob demanded that Pether be handed over to them, or if not that they be paid 'fifty shillings in lieu of the charges they had been at in promoting of the design', which is a little like a burglar demanding compensation because the police caught him before he could find anything worth stealing. But the Cowley men were not cowed so easily; they fought their way out and took Pether with them back to Cowley, where they mounted a twenty-four hour guard over him. By 'subtle contrivances', and probably helped by Pether's own preferences in the affair, St Peter's sneaked him out again to set up another wedding. This time Cowley did not bother engaging directly in battle; they ran to the magistrates at Quarter Sessions and secured a warrant for Pether to be brought into the court. This time they won. Pether never did marry Black Moll, and the plots of the churchwardens of St Peter's were thwarted. In the end, of course, both sides had spent the sort of money which would have kept Black Moll and her child comfortably for quite some time.

Even those marriages which were desired by both parties and went off without a hitch sometimes turned sour quite quickly. The case of Thomas Fortnam and his wife Mary could easily have served as a model for Lady Chatterley, had Fortnam obligingly got himself crippled early on in the proceedings. In this instance it was her mother's shepherd rather than her husband's gamekeeper for whom his wife conceived a sudden passion, but there were several witnesses to voice a similar distaste for the way in which an upper crust lady was demeaning herself with one of the hoary-handed sons of toil.

The Fortnams were married on 19 November 1767 in Steeple Barton, where both Fortnam and his wife's mother, Mary Ibell, had farms. Alas, 'Mary Fortnam, being wholly unmindful of her conjugal vow, and not having the fear of God before her eyes, but being moved and instigated by the Devil', took a shine to the shepherd Thomas Palmer, and the two of them were frequently seen out and about together, walking in the fields, 'and were often observed to kiss each other, and to behave towards each other in a lewd, amorous, indecent manner'. This was bad enough, but Mary then managed to contrive an excuse for their spending the night together. John Carter, one of her mother's servants, had been kicked by a horse and was laid up in bed at his employer's house. Mary suddenly began to profess a most unusual, and indeed downright suspicious, concern for his welfare, and insisted to her husband that she must go to nurse him.

Palmer volunteered to join her in sitting up all night with the sick man; however, the servant was not so sick that he couldn't see what was going on and report on it later. What he saw was 'Mary Fortnam and Thomas Palmer to behave to and with each other in a very amorous and immoderate manner, and to take great liberties and freedom with each other, and to be in very indecent postures together'. Eventually they left the invalid to look after himself while they went downstairs for two hours for purposes unexplained but suspected. The next night they sat up with him again, although they spent the time over by the window of his room, drinking with their arms around one another's waists and 'taking great liberties with one another in a lewd and amorous manner'. This time they didn't even bother to leave the room before getting on with the main business of the evening:

Mary Fortnam several times called out 'John!' (meaning John Carter) who, pretending to be asleep, made no answer. She put out the candle and she and Thomas Palmer came towards John Carter's bed, and she again called out several times 'John!', who made no answer. Then she and Thomas Palmer lay down together on the floor by the side of the bed, and soon after John Carter heard a noise, as if the shoes of Mary or Thomas were scratching against the floor, and heard Mary and Thomas pant and blow, during which time it is believed that Thomas Palmer was upon Mary Fortnam and that they had carnal use of each other's bodies. . . .

After getting away with this, or so they thought, the lovers started to take the kind of risks which might lead psychologists to theorize that subconsciously they wanted to be found out. Mary Ibell went away from home for some days to visit friends, and her daughter immediately offered to move in in her absence to look after the household. The first household task in which she engaged was to move her mother's bed out of the room it shared with the servant Mary Scaresbrook and into the room over the dairy, where she could use it and be undisturbed. She carefully moved it back the day before her mother was due home, apparently thinking that as long as Mary Ibell didn't see it, the fact that every servant in the house knew what had happened didn't matter in the slightest. She believed she now had the perfect rendezvous to share with her shepherd for a whole week.

Thomas Palmer, like the other male servants, shared a room elsewhere in Mary Ibell's house. This made it a little difficult for him to join Mrs Fortnam, but he waited until well after the family had gone to bed one night, then sneaked out of the room to make his way to the dairy. Unfortunately his fellow servant William Stockford heard him go; he in turn got out of bed and woke up another servant, Thomas Bedding, telling him that he thought Palmer had gone to join the temporary mistress of the house. The two of them crept over to the room above the dairy and listening at the door to the proceedings in the room, which reportedly took two hours. At the end of this time Palmer came out of the room dressed only in his shirt and shepherd's frock, and walked straight into the arms of Messrs Bedding and Stockford, who told him that they knew his little game and it wasn't on. Palmer collapsed: 'I will do so no more! I will run away without any wages, for Mr Fortnam will kill me!'

It is difficult to say whether Bedding and Stockford were animated purely by moral disapproval, or whether they just enjoyed having power over people. Their own morals were a trifle suspect, as they promised Palmer they would tell no one, then broadcast the news to all and sundry. For the time being, however, they decided to add Mary Fortnam to the list of their victims, and charged her face to face with adultery. She turned on them venemously: 'If I had asked you to have done the same, to be sure you would have done it!' This wasn't quite the reaction they were hoping for, so they went back to her a few days later and elaborated on what would happen if they told her husband. This had a far more satisfactory effect, as Mary threatened to hang or drown herself if they did so. As it happened, they did but she didn't.

Fortnam promptly separated from his wife and started divorce proceedings, no mean feat at a time when divorce required an expensive Act of Parliament. Most couples in that situation would have been forced to stay together, or at best get a judicial separation *a mensa et thoro* from the Church courts. This was really bad luck on Mary Fortnam, who thereby lost out entirely, being the guilty party in the case. It didn't do much for Thomas Palmer's prospects of continuing employment either.

If you couldn't trust your mother-in-law's shepherd, who could you trust? Well, nobody, judging by some of the cases which turn up in the Church courts and at Quarter Sessions. One item from Quarter Sessions in 1707 provides a classic warning for historians to make sure they've got all the evidence before attempting to draw conclusions from it. A warrant survives in the sessions roll for Easter 1707 to Jonathan Kent, Constable of Henley-on-Thames, for the arrest of one James Lower, on a charge of breaking into the house of Dr John Cawley, Rector of Henley. So far it seems an open and shut case, although sympathetic light is shed on the rector by a letter to the Constable which appears later on the roll:

> Mr Kent – I desire you to use Mr Lower with all civility possible, and give him time enough to get bail, and not to carry him to the Castle [Oxford Castle, the county gaol] but in the greatest necessity, which I hope cannot happen. My service to him. I am your assured friend to serve you – J Cawley

If one happened to miss the third scrap of paper relating to this case on the roll, the enduring picture would be of Lower the worthless malefactor, and the saintly Rector of Henley who forgave him. However, that third document is the examination of Constable Kent before the magistrates: 'On the 8th of February I was sent for by Dr Cawley and by him ordered to arrest Mr James Lower, who had broken open a chamber door in his house. At the same time, the doctor declared he did not believe Lower meant to take anything out of the house, except his own wife, who was at that time in the chamber he broke open.' No, you can't always trust the rector either.

Anthony Rutter of Hailey, near Witney, was a more fortunate man than some, as he was able to trust his wife implicitly. The problem here was that neither of them could trust their neighbour, William Smith of Fenny End. Smith seems to have been trying to set new standards in sexual harassment, and by and large he succeeded. Mary Rutter, by general consent, was 'a woman of good repute and estimation, and of a modest and civil behaviour'. She was also, one is given to understand, very attractive, and thus caught the eye of Smith. The fact that she was already married did not worry him in the slightest; indeed, his predelictions seem to have been such that he considered this a positive advantage. He 'did oftentimes attempt the chastity of Mary Rutter, and would have had the carnal knowledge of her body, and Mary could never be quiet for him, whensoever he had an opportunity of meeting her singly or alone, for the space of three years last past or more, but he was still soliciting and enticeing her to dishonesty'. This had become public knowledge, and must have been more than embarrassing to the Rutters; however, Smith eventually grew tired of these endless discussions and decided to do something a little more practical to further his ends.

Waiting until Anthony Rutter was out of the way, Smith visited his house and manoeuvred himself into one of the bedrooms with Mary, 'and being there alone with her did behave himself very rudely and uncivilly towards her, and would have forced her to lie with him and had the carnal knowledge of her body, and threw her upon the bed by force'. His victim was either too quick or too strong for him, broke away and ran downstairs, but Smith 'did run after her, and did offer and endeavour to carry her upstairs again by force'. He failed, and it may have been this which decided him to sort things out man to man with Anthony. Anthony had something he wanted, namely Mary; Smith had something Anthony wanted, namely the power to leave her alone. He therefore made the husband an offer he found it only too easy to refuse:

> he did report and say in the hearing of credible witnesses that if Anthony Rutter would give him leave to have a leap or two at first upon Mary, and stand at the bed's feet, once a year after should serve his turn, meaning that if Anthony Rutter would stand at the bed's feet and give him leave to lay with Mary his wife, that he might have carnal knowledge of her body once or twice before his face, that once a year after to have her should serve his turn, and then he would agree to be friends with Anthony.

This was obviously a new definition of friendship as far as Rutter was concerned, and one he could do without; he reported Smith to the bishop, and the result was a hefty dose of penance for the importunate neighbour. As far as we know, Mary Rutter was left in peace from then on.

At least she could take some small comfort from the fact that William Smith wanted her for herself. She wasn't being solicited on a commercial basis, which was liable to happen to any presentable woman in the parish of St Thomas, Oxford, around 1716. The reason for this was a certain house of ill fame, established in that neighbourhood by Joseph Anslow and his wife Ann – or at least she *seems* to be his wife, although she sometimes goes under the name of Ann Pemerton, in which guise she has an alternative husband, Charles. An odd household by any definition, it is described by one of the neighbours as a place 'where persons of ill character are harboured all night or very late sometimes, making disturbances and committing great disorders'. Charitably one might argue that the couple was simply trying to make ends meet in a difficult time, as a certain Rachel

Mason swears 'that Joseph Anslow and Ann Pemerton are very poor and indigent, and have very little goods of their own, and have not a good character amongst their neighbours'. However, Rachel had worse to say of them than that, as she recalls that 'about three years ago she was sent for by Ann Anslow to come to her house, and not knowing the business she went, and while she was there she was solicited by Ann Anslow in the presence of her husband to commit the sin of adultery with a person then present, which she refused and never went to the house after'.

If Ann Anslow/Pemerton was in the business of ruining decent women in one way, she had a sideline in ruining their husbands in another. Mary Wells claimed that Ann 'used to send for her husband William, and keep him day and night till he was forced to go away for debt, and he has since sent her word that Ann Anslow ruined him'. Finally the parishioners decided they had had enough of the Anslow household, and took the bull by the horns; they went to Ann 'and asked her why she would keep a scandalous house and entertain all sort of persons of ill fame and make disturbances among her neighbours'. Her response made up in candour what it lacked in the way of rational explanation: 'Call me what you will, you cannot call me worse than I am!' Just to underline the point, she then imported 'a woman of vile character, who within two or three months gave one of the soldiers the pox'.

Charles Pemerton, who claimed that he did not live with his wife because of her scandalous character, and because he once caught her in bed with another man, did what he could to improve the quality of life in St Thomas'. He hired one William Hearne to take her to Bampton, her home town, to lodge her there for a while at his expense and keep her out of the way. Unfortunately her fame preceded her. The Bampton parish officials, and the man in whose house she was intended to lodge, 'refused to admit her to stay, by reason she was a person of very ill fame, and a lewd person, and they feared their houses would be burnt by her, accounting her a very malicious person'. Nowhere else is there a suggestion that she was an arsonist in addition to her other talents, but perhaps they were prepared to accuse her of anything just to keep her out, or perhaps the accusation was metaphorical. At any rate, 'in a little time Ann Pemerton was sent home from Bampton', and St Thomas' was lumbered once again; so, of course, was husband Charles, who was in no position to go through the very expensive process of a divorce. Thomas Fortnam's solution to a far less outrageous wife was simply not available to him. Nor, it seems, did he wish to go to the lengths of certain other husbands, who had their own ways of dealing with wives who, for one reason or another, had become inconvenient.

One such husband was John Godfrey. He had married his wife Elizabeth on 19 August 1706, after coming to a very profitable agreement with her relations concerning her marriage portion: he had 'money and lands given him to the value of six hundred pounds, besides goods of great value'. He then took her off to his house at Milton, where he underwent a sudden and most disturbing transformation from a plausible suitor into something a lot more sinister. Having got the money he was stuck with the wife; he certainly had no affection for her, but one gets the impression that he still liked having her around for the sheer pleasure of making her life a misery:

> Without any provocation he called her bitch, whore, devil, and said that he had married the spawn of the devil, and that he could not have found such another woman without going to hell for one. And that he should hate her as long as she lived. And that he only married her to be a plague to her. And he has threatened to bring home a child of unknown parents to be kept by her. And he hath very often bid her be gone from him, saying that she should never have a groat from him, and if he could hinder it no one should give her a bit of bread. And that she should not be another night in his house. And if she stayed there he would never own or treat her as a wife, or give her any better language. And at other times he would in a rude, surly manner command her to his bed, saying 'You bitch, you shall lie with me!', which she has sometimes refused to do, fearing he would do her some private mischief. He has called her common whore, naming several persons, and declaring that if she had a child he would not own it. And he has often threatened to lock her up in her chamber, and to hold her behind the fire and burn her.
>
> When she has been at her private devotions, Mr Godfrey would come into the room under her closet and call to her, saying 'Where are you, you bitch? What, are you praying to the Devil? Come down, you whore!' Near the time the sacrament was to be administered, he used several angry expressions to deter her from going to it. And when he understood she had received it, he would often tell her that she was damned, and that if she did not go to the devil he would go thither for her. She was forced to go to the Church on foot, though her house was near half a mile from it and the season dirty and he himself riding thither at the same time.

Godfrey was not a nice man, it seems; still, up to that point it is only her word against his. However, other voices then join in. The Revd William Best of Hillingworth, Warwickshire, the home of Elizabeth's family, had known her for many years and swore that her reputation was without blemish, religious and charitable. Her maid testified that she had actually been present when Godfrey had tried to burn his wife and had helped to prevent him, in payment for which he had beaten her and threatened to murder her. Finally Mrs Godfrey could stand it no longer; she had to escape from him. The problem was how to go about it. In the late twentieth century there is concern about the difficulties beaten wives experience in trying to leave their husbands; three hundred years ago there was simply nowhere to run to. Hillingworth was days away, even if she had the fare for transport. Her only recourse was to throw herself on the mercy of two men, John Crispe and Samuel Cleaver, who were visiting her husband. Horrified by her story, they agreed to take her away from the house, but not, apparently, without difficulty; Godfrey was not about to let his tame victim leave without a fight. In the course of the proceedings, he assaulted Crispe, who took him to court for it; he ended up being fined 40s. (£2), but that is a trivial sum compared with the value of his wife's dowry, which he presumably kept.

The Godfrey saga is unpleasant enough; the Staniford case is grisly to a degree which would be comic, if one could forget that real people were involved. Lettice Carter was the daughter of Richard Carter the elder, a prominent citizen of Oxford around the time of the Civil War – a brewer, a freeman of the city, and a member of the Council holding a variety of offices. His son Richard followed in his footsteps, and his daughter Jane married the tanner John Cogbill, who was also a freeman and a city councillor. Lettice, however, made a far less advantageous match, in a number of ways. She married Francis Staniford, a tailor, in 1653, and over the following decade grew to regret the fact.

Although the couple had children in 1655 and 1657, their married life seems to have become increasingly acrimonious and violent. The difference between Staniford and Godfrey appears to be that while the latter enjoyed tormenting his wife and keeping her in constant fear that he might harm her, the former dispensed with all the sinister, psychological stuff. He just tried to kill her, frequently:

Francis Staniford did take a sword which he called his bilbow, and did run it freely at Lettice, his wife, saying he would kill her, but missing her body he ran it through her clothes, with that force that he stuck it in the wainscot with his sword through her clothes.

He did run at her with a stiletto knife, saying he would kill her.

He did throw a pair of tailor's shears at her, swearing 'I will kill thee!', and, missing her narrowly, stuck them in a post that was behind her, and said, 'I must be hanged for killing thee'.

He did run fiercely at Lettice his wife with a spit, and with a resolution as he then said himself to run her through, but some persons being in the room did put him by, and so she escaped.

He took up an andiron, and hit Lettice his wife on the face with it, and wounded her so that it caused her to lay under the surgeon's hands a long time before she could be healed.

He did throw Lettice down a pair of stairs when she was big with child and wanted not above three weeks to the time of her delivery, and afterwards when she was so thrown down by him, he went and trod upon her.

He made it his constant course to beat her from time to time, and has been seen to beat her several times with a bedstaff whilst she lay in her bed, and has oftentimes said that he would keep a whore under her nose.

He did beat her out of his house and shut the door after her, and swore that if she came within the doors again, he would be the death of her.

He said that he would strip her skin over her ears and raze her bones.

He did declare that if ever he saw her any more he would rip up her guts and slit her nostrils, and this he bound with grievous oaths, and said more that he would be the death of her.

Either he was staggeringly incompetent or she was very lucky, as after a decade of marriage she was still in one piece. She was also of the opinion that a change of habitation would do her no end of good, and left to return to her parents' home. One might expect the next stage to be a lawsuit by Lettice's family against Staniford for assault, or even a petition for divorce. If so, one would be disappointed. In fact, it was Staniford himself who went to court and brought a case against Richard Carter senior, Richard Carter junior and John Cogbill for detaining his wife – the one he had sworn he never wanted to see again – and depriving him of his conjugal rights. Judging that he included assault and battery as part and parcel of these rights, the Carter family refused to give her up, and the case turned into one of formal separation. Procurators were appointed by both parties, and Francis was cited to appear before the court in March 1663, but he failed to turn up. Twice more he was cited, and twice more did not appear. Then in April it is noted that the parties had come to an accord. The precise nature of it is uncertain, but it may be that Staniford was simply too ill to do his wife any more harm. Eight months later he died. Could his deranged behaviour have been part of a slow disease which eventually killed him?

Certainly there was no reconciliation, because Lettice renounced any right to her deceased husband's estate. On a happier note, she later married one Henry Phillipps, and there is no record of her having similar problems again.

The rich could divorce; the poor could at least achieve a separation from bed and board; both groups could simply kill their partners if they thought they could get away with it. But there was one further way of disposing of an unwanted helpmeet.

In 1696 George Fuller decided he had had enough of his wife, so he did what he would have done with any of his possessions: he took her down to the market in Chinnor and put her up for sale. At the very reasonable price of 2¼d. a pound [almost exactly 1p], he soon had a taker in the shape of one Thomas Heath. The unfortunate woman was loaded on to the scales and was knocked down to the purchaser for 29s. ¼d. – you'd think he could have knocked the odd farthing off – which suggests that she weighed in at a fraction over eleven stone. Then Thomas Heath kissed her before her husband to cement the bargain and took her away.

Who ended up in court as a result of this day's work? The astute will have guessed the answer; it was Thomas Heath, on a charge of adultery. It was difficult to find a law against conducting an invalid wife sale, but perfectly easy to nab someone for sleeping with a woman who was still legally married to another man. However, Heath claimed he had done nothing of the sort, and indeed comes out of the story as something of a knight on a white charger. After buying her, he took her to a public house in Thame, where she stayed for two days, but during that time he did not see her for more than one hour a day. Then he took her on to the White Hart in Benson for the night (where he did sit on the side of her bed, but denies ever getting into it), and from there conveyed her down to London, where he handed her over to the safekeeping of her brother. Far from being a lascivious rogue, Heath turned out to be in much the same category as Crispe and Cleaver who had fought their way out of William Godfrey's house to get his wife back to her family. It's refreshing to find a few gentlemen among the sinners and villains of Oxfordshire.

CHAPTER THREE

UNIVERSITY RAG

While the average sinner or villain might well remain in the village of his or her birth, in the same walk of life, for the whole of an earthly span, some chose to better themselves with an education. They were not invariably the most intelligent, but usually the richest. Claims that Oxford University can be traced back to the Roman occupation of Britain (the record office is the proud possessor of a volume which seeks to prove precisely that) should be treated with some suspicion, but no one is going to dispute its medieval origins. Practically as old is the legendary rivalry between Oxford and Cambridge; indeed one of the earliest stories of the university takes the rivalry as its theme.

To the south side of the town, the river is crossed by Folly Bridge. At some point, probably in the late thirteenth century, the New Gate was built on it, and there are notes of repairs made to it throughout the following three hundred years. Above it rose the gatehouse, known as Friar Bacon's Study because of the belief that Roger Bacon had used it as an observatory in its early years. Bacon, whose achievements range through philosophy, theology, linguistics and science, dreamed up the concept of a lighter-than-air machine well before da Vinci, and ought to be the patron saint of archivists as he invented the magnifying glass; there must be a gloomy moral to be drawn from the fact that the man who was known in his lifetime as the Wonderful Doctor is probably lying in an unmarked grave under the St Ebbe's multi-storey car park.

Nevertheless, the highly suspect story goes, Bacon was very much alive when a party of Cambridge students came up what is now the Abingdon Road one evening in the 1290s. The inter-varsity loathing was doing well at the time, and the Cambridge students had decided to visit Oxford in order to force a disputation with their opposite numbers and prove once and for all that Cambridge was the better university. Arriving at the gate they called up to the man they assumed to be the gatekeeper — who else would you expect to find in a gatehouse around midnight? – and just to show what they were made of, they called up in Latin.

Bacon, somewhat irritated at the interruption to his astronomy, called down a reply; instinctively he used the same language. There was a brief conference at the foot of the gatehouse, concerning the incidence of gatekeepers who were fluent in Latin and the probable abilities of the students in a town where Classics scholars got the jobs which went to illiterates in Cambridge. After which, the Cambridge students turned round and went back the way they had come, while Bacon got back to his stargazing. Naturally, as an Oxford man, I believe every word of it, and I try not to think what a very odd direction the Cambridge students chose from which to approach Oxford.

There is no doubt whatsoever of a far more violent dispute, between the scholars of Oxford and their other famous enemies: the townsfolk. The Town v. Gown antagonism is as old as the university, but at no time did it flare up so disastrously as in 1354, when the notorious St Scholastica riot took place. On the south-west corner of Carfax, still commemorated by a stone set in the wall of the present building, stood the Swindlestock tavern. On 10 February, St Scholastica's Day, a number of students were drinking there, including Walter de Springheuse and Roger de Chesterfield; they were brought wine by the vintner, John de Croydon, but turned their noses up at it, little realizing the future consequences of their action.

They told Croydon his wine was bad. He told them there was nothing wrong with it. They repeated the charge and, just to underline the point, broke a jar of it over his head. Croydon staggered out and recounted the story to his neighbours, presumably with a number of suitable embellishments. This was the excuse the townsfolk had been looking for. Tensions had been growing in the past few years, and the Swindlestock incident lit the powder keg. The town bell at St Martin's church, opposite the tavern, was rung to summon the townspeople together, and when the students strolled out of the Swindlestock they had about three seconds to be very, very surprised before their energies were taken up in fighting off the mob.

The Chancellor of the University, having been told that trouble was brewing, came running down to Carfax in an attempt to calm both sides, but after ducking a hail of hostile arrows he decided that discretion was the better part of valour, and ran. Reaching St Mary's church, further up the High Street, he rang the university bell, putting the students on the alert, and battle was joined in earnest. The two sides, armed to the teeth, fought until the evening, but by some miracle no one was seriously hurt. This was not at all what the townsfolk had intended, so they gathered together to plan how a lot of people could be seriously hurt the following day.

On the 11th, a Wednesday, the chancellor arrived in formal procession at Carfax to proclaim peace, but the city bailiffs had other ideas. They had already sent a message round to selected townsmen that they should be ready to come out armed against the students when the town bell was rung, and to make the odds a little more uneven they sent round to the neighbouring villages, inviting their more bloodthirsty inhabitants to join the fray. At first an uneasy kind of peace prevailed. A group of scholars went walking after dinner in Beaumont, believing that the violence was over, and failed to notice that they were being shadowed by a collection of townsmen armed with bows and arrows. When the townsmen attacked they barely had a chance. Some of them made it to shelter in the Augustinian Priory, but the ones who ran towards the town were badly wounded, and one of them was trapped and killed just outside the walls. At that moment the town bell began to ring.

As befitted their training the students acted logically. In a straight fight between them and the townsmen they might have a chance; if reinforcements from the villages joined in to help the town they were finished. Their first move, therefore, was to block all the town gates; then they set about the townsfolk in earnest, and by all accounts were doing rather well when the countrymen broke in through the West Gate. After that, the battle was a foregone conclusion. The townsmen broke open the students' halls, killing or maiming anyone they found, and destroying their goods or carrying them away as plunder. The carnage lasted into the Thursday, with the townsmen slaughtering any who stood against them and throwing their bodies into cesspits and dunghills, until all the students who were not dead had fled the town.

The townsmen's carnage had lasted two days. The university's revenge lasted five hundred years.

During the riot the king, who was staying at his palace in Woodstock, had sent an order to cease fighting, which had been judiciously ignored. This was a bad move. Once calm had returned he sent word of the town's punishment. Most of its hard-won privileges were taken from it and granted instead to the university. In addition the Bishop of Lincoln forbade administration of the sacrament to any townsfolk. The bailiffs petitioned for mitigation of the sentence, but were ignored. Only in 1357 were their privileges returned, but on one condition. Every St Scholastica's Day from then on, the town was obliged to say a number of masses for the souls of the students killed. In addition the mayor and bailiffs, with sixty of the chief burgesses, had to attend St Mary's church and swear observance of the customary rights of the university. The penalty for failing to do this was 100 marks. This annual reminder was most humiliating for the town, and they

Friar Bacon's Study on Folly Bridge, the ideal vantage point for humiliating Cambridge students (*Centre for Oxfordshire Studies*)

Carfax and the Swindlestock tavern – scene of the great St Scholastica's Day riot (*Centre for Oxfordshire Studies*)

The Town v. Gown riots continued long after St Scholastica's Day, as this eighteenth-century cartoon shows (*Centre for Oxfordshire Studies*)

looked for ways to wriggle out of it. On the pretext that masses had been abolished under Queen Elizabeth, they refused to enact the penance for fifteen years. This landed them with a fine of 1,500 marks. In 1800 the mayor, Richard Cox, refused to attend at St Mary's to perform penance for an event four and a half centuries old, now scarcely more than a legend; the university had him fined 100 marks. Only in 1825 was the punishment finally lifted, by which time it had ensured that the Town v. Gown antagonism was a fact of life.

The university, however, continued to grow and prosper. Not only were the colleges gradually established, but certain other institutions now eternally associated with it arose, such as the Bodleian Library and the Ashmolean Museum. Both benefited considerably from gifts of private collections in their early stages. The original university library was effectively ruined under Edward VI, and only towards the end of Elizabeth's reign did Thomas Bodley take it in hand, refit it, and give it 2,000 books as the basis of its collections. Subsequent donors included the Earl of Pembroke, who was persuaded by Archbishop Laud to hand over his Greek manuscripts, and Thomas Selden, who donated not only his books but also a remarkable collection of spectacles, which he was accustomed to use as bookmarks, then forget where he had put them. In fact, Selden was intending to leave his library to the Inner Temple as a protest against the Bodleian refusing to let him borrow books, though fortunately he never did so.

But no donor to the library was as odd as the founder of the museum.

Elias Ashmole first arrived in Oxford in 1644 as a Royalist commissioner of excise, and entered Brasenose College, though in what capacity is uncertain; he may simply have been quartered there. Being a man with strong ideas on what he wanted out of life he soon married a wealthy widow, twenty years his senior, which gave him the financial support and leisure to pursue his interests. Those interests were very simple: he wanted to be an antiquarian.

His character included traits popularly associated with antiquarianism, though not in fact necessary to it; he was a firm believer in astrology, and the sort of folk medicine which involved hanging three dead spiders around his neck to cure the ague. It also included aspects not generally associated with antiquarianism, but in fact absolutely vital, such as being completely ruthless. In 1659 he met the greatest collector of curiosities of the age, Tradescant, who owned what was popularly called the Ark, a ragbag of eccentricities from all over the globe, which was the prototype of the modern, far more scientifically organized, museum. Tradescant and his wife had no children, and Ashmole so impressed them that they determined to give him the Ark after their respective deaths, even drawing up a deed of gift to that end.

It therefore came as something of a surprise to Ashmole, when Tradescant died in 1662, to find that there was no mention of the Ark coming to him in the will. Notwithstanding this he demanded it from the widow and received a dusty answer. He therefore preferred a bill in Chancery against her, to relieve her of her property. Apparently the stipulation that he was to receive the Ark after *both* the Tradescants had died weighed with him not in the least; the collector was dead, so he wanted it. The case dragged on for sixteen years, until events provided the conditions for Ashmole's inheritance; Mrs Tradescant was found drowned in the fishpond at the bottom of her garden. Her misfortune was Oxford's gain, for two years later Ashmole had the collection moved to the city, and it formed the basis of the earliest public museum in England.

No one ever suggested, at least publicly, that Ashmole had been instrumental in solving his own inheritance problems. If he had it would scarcely have been out of the ordinary for a university in which, it has been maliciously said, contenders for place battle the more vindictively because the stakes are so small. In 1639 a Wadham undergraduate was so angry with the two fellows of the college who had sent him down, that he lured them to an inn and stabbed them. There have been dark comments about the passing of more than one college head, and not all of them a matter of ancient history. But how much easier if one can simply prevent one's disliked rival taking over the college in the first place.

The pattern for modern day college life is largely due to Walter de Merton, who realized that the earlier system of students living in lodgings or tenements gave little formal control, and looked for a way of putting them under the direct control of tutors and governors. His own college set the style by being self-governing with a visitor, the Archbishop of Canterbury. Whenever the wardenship of Merton College fell vacant, the fellows were to choose three possible candidates and present them to the archbishop, who would then make his choice. This was all very well until 1562, when the fellows argued about the nominations, broke into various factions and ended up presenting five candidates to the primate, three of whom had never seen the inside of the college. This gave Archbishop Parker the chance to get his own way; he ignored all the candidates and put in his own nominee, John Manne, sometime fellow of New College.

The wardenship was not due to be filled until the end of March, and so, in the absence of the new warden, the college was run by the sub-warden, William Hawle, who found the situation suited him very well. Hawle was a Roman Catholic of the old school, and he took the opportunity to reintroduce certain Catholic practices, such as the singing of particular hymns in hall on holy days, and vigils from All Saints to the evening of the Purification. Many of the older fellows were behind him, and he was beginning to enjoy getting things back to normal when the new warden turned up. A nominee of Parker, he was obviously going to ruin everything.

Manne turned up on 30 March, accompanied by the vice chancellor and others, and formally demanded admittance. Hawle refused, on the grounds that he should not be there before 2 April, and sent him away. This gave him three days' grace, and he used them to decide on desperate measures. When Manne arrived at 9 a.m. on the 2nd he found the college gates locked. Hawle was obviously prepared to withstand a siege, but never got the chance. Manne sent for John Broke, one of the senior fellows, and made a deal with him to unlock the gate when Hawle's back was turned. Thus the warden made a rather unprepossessing entrance, but the fact that he was in at all angered Hawle so much that he made the fatal mistake of hitting Manne, which led to his being dismissed by the archbishop. His supporters were dealt with by the new warden in short order; some voluntarily resigned, and two were dismissed on a trumped-up charge of perjury. Broke should have lived long and prospered, but in fact he suffered the traditional traitor's fate of being turned on by the party to which he had defected. Having installed himself comfortably the new warden took a look at Broke's accounts as bursar, and found that he had been systematically defrauding the college. He went the same way as Hawle.

The quarrel between Hawle and Manne is easy enough to explain; that between Harry Barker, Vice-President of Trinity College, and Thomas Sykes, the college bursar, is far more puzzling. In 1689 Sykes was one of the scrutators for the election of fellows of the college. As the various members of the college came up to write their choices on the paper, Sykes covered over what each previous member had written, to preserve some semblance of a secret ballot. Barker seemed to take some objection to this, telling Sykes that 'he need not have laid his hand upon the paper, but it was his breeding', repeating the words several times in the hearing of the college president and various fellows, and adding that Sykes was a saucy fellow, just in case his meaning wasn't clear. There seems to have been some envy involved in Barker's malevolence, as he went on to say that Sykes 'valued himself as a doctor for his scarf, but that he, Harry Barker, was a better man than he there, and as good or better anywhere else, and that if Dr Sykes did know what others thought of him, he would not take himself for so fine a fellow'. He then made a fist at the astonished bursar and said, 'If I had you in another place alone . . .', with a meaningful pause.

Sykes applied to the president, who had heard the exchange, and said,

'Sir, these words are neither fit for me to hear or bear, nor him to give,' but the president affected to take no notice. There was nothing Sykes could do, but he soon found out that Barker's ill-will was not going to stop there, and the vice president started a positive vendetta against him.

On 13 July Barker peremptorily summoned Sykes to the buttery before two of the junior fellows, Barber and Wake, and immediately began to question him, in the presence of various college servants, about a key to the chapel. Sykes agreed that he had kept the key for some time, at which Barker cried, 'This is a brave thing! Here is a key kept clandestinely and so the goods may be stolen out of the chapel, and who shall be accountable for them?' He demanded the return of the key, which Sykes brought out of his pocket and handed over, thereby defusing the situation. Evidently Barker did not want it defused, as he then attacked Sykes about his servant, saying that the man was an impudent, saucy fellow, and warned him to turn the man out. Warming to his theme he told Sykes that 'he discountenanced the discipline of the college, and countenanced those who lived irregularly, and that he made it his business to make quarrels in the college by speaking ill of the fellows behind their backs among his companions'.

By now Sykes was getting angry, and he declared that he kept his prayers and did his duty as much as any man, nor had he ever spoken against any of the fellows, but Barker claimed 'that he had spoke against every one of them, and particularly he had said that Mr Wake was a very rogue, and he had likewise spoke against Mr Barber'. Sykes solemnly denied it, but Barker replied, 'No doubt you are innocent, you will never mend, you will die as the whore or bawd said, with a good conscience in your calling'. 'You once had a better opinion of me,' said Sykes; indeed, replied Barker, but he had now found the bursar to be a knave.

It may be that Sykes was already considering counter-action against the vice-president, as he took the college statutes to his room and started to study them in some detail. Barker heard about this on the 16th, and lost no time in visiting Sykes and demanding them back. The bursar handed them over, asking when he might have them again, but Barker said he was not allowed to take them to his room, but must read them in the vice-president's chamber. Very well, answered Sykes, but could he at least have permission to transcribe the passage he needed? Barker refused to commit himself, leaving the impression that it very much depended what the passage was.

Barker then left town for a week. This might not sound anything out of the ordinary, but the president himself was not in Oxford at the time, and for his deputy to be absent as well was unusual. Still, there was an official procedure to be followed in such cases; all formal documents were to be

Merton College, where the fellows barred the gate to keep the new warden out (*Oxfordshire Archives*)

Balliol and Trinity, arch rivals, on and off, through the centuries (*Oxfordshire Archives*)

The legendary Benjamin Jowett, nineteenth-century Master of Balliol (*Oxfordshire Archives*)

handed over to the most senior fellow of the college, so that business could be transacted as usual in his absence. Instead, Barker made up a new procedure. He appointed a temporary vice-president, an unheard-of action, and gave the job to Barber, one of the most junior fellows in college. There seems no reason for him to do this, except that he had already poisoned Barber's mind against Sykes, and could therefore be reasonably sure that Sykes would not get at the college statutes by any means except over Barber's dead body. This did not stop Sykes trying. At first he asked Barber civilly, but the junior fellow replied, 'You know that Mr Vice-President Barker denied your having them to your chamber on Saturday night.' Sykes then insisted, and Barber finally agreed to go and look for them in Barker's room; he returned claiming that he couldn't find them, which did neither his nor Barker's credit any good with the fellows, who realized that if any college business needed to be transacted urgently they were in trouble.

Barker's vindictiveness was getting out of hand. Sykes refused to turn away his servant, so when the vice-president returned, he called Sykes before him and Barber and censured him to lose his commons for a month, 'and if he did not submit within that time to turn away his man, then to lose his fellowship'. This time he had gone too far. The fellows of Trinity petitioned their visitor, the Bishop of Winchester, that,

> Harry Barker is a troublesome, passionate, petulant and tyrannical person, given to strike in his passion and to use injurious and opprobrious language and to make unstatutable orders, and as such reputed to be by all or most of the fellows of Trinity College, and they are justly grieved at the insolent and injurious behaviour of Harry Barker, therefore out of their tender care of the good of the college they do humbly pray to the Lord Bishop that he will be pleased to suspend and inhibit the aforesaid Harry Barker from all exercise of the office of Vice-President.

For once the story had the requisite fairy-tale ending; not only did Sykes beat Barker, but he ended up as president of the college and, according to the antiquary Hearne, 'a great tutor, an honest man, and a learned Divine'. In Hearne's terminology, that simply means that he was a Jacobite.

Ill will between colleges was more prevalent than ill will inside them; Trinity, for example, was more interested in attacking Balliol than in its own squabbles. During the Civil War Balliol's fortunes fell to a low point, while Trinity was continuing to flourish. Not content with merely gloating over this, Bathurst, the president of Trinity, amused himself by wandering round the neighbouring college in the evening, throwing rocks through any windows which were not already broken. The rivalry continued, though in a more light-hearted way, into the nineteenth century and the mastership of Benjamin Jowett at Balliol. The Jowett stories, many of them apocryphal, would fill a volume in themselves; however, one of the less frequently quoted ones concerns the college rivalry.

During the Victorian era the concept that small is beautiful had made little headway; rather, many people thought wistfully of a giant college, dwarfing its Oxford companions, which by its very size could become the greatest seat of learning in the world. Jowett put the proposal to Raper of Trinity that if the three colleges on the site north of Broad Street – Balliol, Trinity and St John's – joined together, the result would achieve precisely that aim. Of course, he said, the resultant college would have to be named after the oldest foundation which, as it happened, was Balliol. Raper listened to him gravely, seemed to take him seriously, and said he would have to consult his senior common room. A short while later they met again. Raper reported that his fellows were all in favour of the idea. There was just one point, he said. The new college would, of course, be three colleges in one. Logically, therefore, it ought to be called Trinity. The suggestion was never heard of again.

The nineteenth century seems to have spawned a fine crop of eccentrics in the university. If one were offering prizes, the Buckland family would probably come first, working as a team. Professor William Buckland of Christ Church, the first Professor of Geology, kept a very odd household in Tom Quad. W. Tuckwell used to play with Buckland's son Frank, and left a vivid picture of life with the professor in his *Reminiscences of Oxford*:

> I recall the queer dishes garnishing the dinner table – horseflesh I remember more than once, crocodile another day, mice baked in batter on a third day – while the guinea-pig under the table inquiringly nibbled at your infantine toes, the bear walked round your chair and rasped your hand with file-like tongue, the jackal's fiendish yell close by came through the open window. Frank used to tell of their visit to a foreign cathedral, where was exhibited a martyr's blood – dark spots on the pavement, ever fresh and ineradicable. The professor dropped on the pavement and touched the stain with his tongue. 'I can tell you what it is; it is bat's urine!'

Surely Buckland was an eccentric rather than a villain? Not according to certain individuals at Nuneham. Buckland's hobby was eating, not in the sense of a gourmet, but rather trying to eat his way through every living being. After all, how does one know that something is not fit to eat until one has tried it? Moles brought him up short for a while, and were top of his list of inedibles, but he later replaced them with bluebottles. It might, therefore, have been considered unwise to show him anything which he hadn't already tasted, but this consideration did not occur to the proud possessors of the heart of a King of France, carefully preserved in a snuff box at Nuneham Park. 'I have eaten some strange things,' said Buckland, 'but never the heart of a King.' Before anyone could stop him, he proceeded to remedy the omission.

With this sort of upbringing, it is hardly surprising that Frank grew to resemble his father. Although he tried to keep his pets out of the rest of the college he was not altogether successful. His bear once joined in morning service at the cathedral, and indeed was left to read the first lesson, when the undergraduate who was in the middle of doing so when the bear arrived left in some haste. On another occasion his eagle dropped into the eight o'clock service, to the fury of the dean. Frank too enjoyed a varied menu, and kept an eye on various zoos for when their rarer species died. He missed the death of a panther at the Surrey Zoological Gardens by a couple of days but, nothing daunted, asked the keeper to dig up the body and send him some chops. He didn't enjoy them.

But in some ways the best sort of sinner is not one who sins extensively, nor who glories in his sin, but one who should be expected, like Caesar's wife, to be above suspicion. Ask any British subject what they know about George Washington beyond the fact that he spent a certain amount of his time as President of the United States, and nine out of ten will probably come up with a story about the young lad chopping down an cherry tree, for reasons which seem to be unclear, and then putting the finger on himself by claiming 'I cannot tell a lie'. This sort of blameless paragon should surely come from a long line of forebears of the utmost probity and rectitude, but not so. His great-great-grandfather, Lawrence, was a Brasenose man, not in itself a sign of degeneracy and debauchery, but one who left the college under something of a cloud.

Washington entered the college in 1619, when he shared chambers with one Atherton Burch. Burch had previously shared with Richard Parre, later Bishop of Sodor and Man, and Washington took over the share of the furnishings which Parre had put into the chambers, valued at £20. He later added £15 worth of furnishings himself. Some time later, he went on an extended journey, and when he returned he found that Burch had died, and the entire contents of the room had been seized by an Oxford tradesman, rejoicing in the prosaic name of John Browne. He sued out a complaint against Browne, but the tradesman came back with a sheaf of evidence that Washington was in debt to him for a small fortune – an original sum of £69

18s, a further bond for £140, and sundry odd sums later. He managed to get £50 of this back, but then Washington suddenly went missing, having 'left his fellowship and abode in the University of Oxon'. This annoyed Browne no end, but the college authorities were far more concerned with their own problems; Washington still owed Brasenose 17s 10d [89p] on his own account, and £9 5s 9d [£9.28] for his pupils' battels. Beside his entry in the bursar's accounts is written: 'Mr Washington to be sued'.

In fact the college seems to have left Washington alone, and after his great-great-grandson made good the story of the debt became an occasional high table joke. Thus it was, in 1924, that a party of American and Canadian lawyers visited Brasenose, and after lunch were told the saga. Immediately one of them asked if the college would be prepared to waive the interest on the debt. On being assured that they would, he organized a quick silver collection, and mock-solemnly presented the Principal with the exact sum of Washington's debt, to salve the family honour of America's first president. Unfortunately this elegant gesture called down a storm of fury on the poor lawyers' heads when they returned home. A number of obsessive patriots simply refused to believe that a member of the Washington family would run away from bad debts, and claimed that the lawyers had compromised the Washington name. The current head of the family denounced the whole affair. But the evidence remains, safe in the college archives.

CHAPTER FOUR

CLERICAL ERROR

What do you do when you've finished the trials and tribulations of university? In my days as an Oxford undergraduate there was a somewhat exaggerated joke that the university appointments people advised everyone they could lay their hands on to become an accountant. There are times when I wish that they had and I had; however, before the present century there was a much more usual course of action for graduates to take. If you had a degree and nowhere else to go, you became a clergyman.

This tendency for the Church to be regarded as a trade rather than a vocation may throw some light on the characters of certain churchmen in the diocese. While it is unquestionably true that being a Christian involves recognizing and combating your own imperfections rather than being perfect, a hard-line minority of Oxfordshire's clerics seem to have persisted in ignoring their own imperfections and gleefully adding to them. This fact was openly, if sadly, acknowledged by the more perceptive bishops. Particularly clear-eyed was 'Soapy' Sam Wilberforce, who kept a book of memoranda on the clergy of his diocese, enabling him to keep track of them and events concerning them. This was not unusual; slightly more unusual was the uninhibited way in which he describes the ministers under his care. Some escaped with their reputations untarnished:

Cumnor: Francis George Henley – a good account of him in his work from Mr James Ashurst, laborious beyond most. Willing to go out night after night to night school.

Some were simply not the right type:

Culham: Walker – an essentially vulgar man . . . Dodson loud in his complaints of Walker's mismanagement of James Morrell . . .

Some had the wrong kind of wives:

Datchet: Mrs Hall — tall, puritan, sour looking person, and very uncourteous in discourse.

Some were distinctly odd:

Newport Pagnell: The Rev S Morley — a man strange beyond measure. Held a meeting for the Diocesan Church Building in schoolroom, Sep 26 1855, advertised on his church door, but he absent! Will not visit the girls' school, because it is indecent, nor suffer his wife to do so, because her place is in the nursery!

Some were downright sinister:

Longworth: The Rev Owen Jenkins — Mr James Hirsey, farmer, first writes and then, Oct 29 1857, comes to me at Clifton and charges Jenkins with adultery with his wife, now penitent and distracted. A child born and buried; he suspects foul play . . .'

The memoranda books are part of Wilberforce's administrative system, which was remarkably good; he is generally credited with having galvanized and reorganized the diocese after it had spent quite some time in the doldrums. In fact, Oxford diocese started in a distinctly shaky manner back in 1542; for the first hundred years of its existence it spent far more time without a bishop than with one — never a good start for a young see — which meant that a lot of responsibility fell on the archdeacon and on the senior officials of the Church, men like the registrar and the chancellor. This would have been less of a problem had they been capable of getting on with one another or even exercising a little mutual toleration, but they weren't. The earliest surviving letter in the diocesan correspondence books sums up the problem perfectly. Dated 1 August 1635, from Registrar Gregory Ballard to Chancellor Dr Zouche, it is a masterpiece of sustained invective, suggesting that their animosity had already gone much too far for a reconciliation:

Sir — You have always been my adversary, as malicious as undeserved; since I have not wronged you, nor deserved this your usage, I scorn to beg your favour. You have thrown dust in my face, you have maliciously slandered me to my betters and your own. I may chance to spatter you! Besides all your false accusations and practices against me, you have most unjustly and indiscreetly disgraced me this day in court. I hope your articles will be drawn up home, yourself, your assistants, and the learned Proctor conspiring, but I pray you, Sir, do not put in that at a public feast at a neighbour college I was so drunk that I was fain to be conveyed home privately to my own house and helped to bed by strangers. I never wore a discoloured eye, to argue me guilty of that which you behind my back accuse me of, nor my wife never called me drunkard, nor base sot, with other aggravations which may be pretended. Sir, know I am as honest as yourself, I understand my duty as you do your command, and I am faithful to my Lord, to whom you are perfidious in these your practices, and hence is your hatred to me. You go about to betray the right of your benefactor, and to oppress him that desired to be your servant. I hold my office by as good a title as yourself, and receive nothing from you. I will give you due respect, but the more you blow, the faster I will hold my cloak. I should have more patience to perish deservedly than to suffer this and these indignities at your hands so unjustly. You account me a prostitute fool and easily to be borne down by your oppression. But, good Dr Zouche, observe this: I know myself so innocent, so absolutely entire from any practice or actual contempt against you, that I will rather beg my bread at your neighbour's door than my pardon at yours, which I hear you threat you will make me do. And this I give you under my hand, which I will never deny, and rest

yours as you please
Gregory Ballard

With an opening flourish like that, the future administrative problems of the diocese pale into insignificance. Compared with a battle between the bishop's own officials, difficulties with rectors or vicars are a trivial matter, let alone squabbles with curates. Although one might have had difficulty convincing John de la Bere, Vicar of Burford, Taynton and Great Barrington, of the fact. A century and a half later he had so much difficulty with his curate, Waldron, that he probably pined for an opponent like Dr Zouche. Zouche seems to have spent a good deal of his time sober, and if he went in for perfidious practices at least he didn't number forgery among his talents.

De la Bere tolerated his curate for some time before deciding that he had to go, and acquainted the bishop with the fact:

I am truely concerned that the misconduct of my curate is become extremely flagrant, and I have given him notice to leave. . . . For the last three months, instances of his intoxication attended with shocking oaths, imprecations, and coming home at all hours of the night have been so frequent, not only our domestic peace but the repose of my parishioners has been often disturbed by his midnight revels. His conversation is so gross and indecent, it is more suited to the walls of a brothel than the sober, decorous habitation of a minister of the gospel. When I last remonstrated with him, he replied with the most horrid execrations, 'I was drunk yesterday, I am drunk today (which was but too true), and I will be drunk tomorrow on Sunday, and let your flock see that in my cups I can do the duty full as well, if not better, than you!'

Many people today are forced to live next door to someone very like that; however, he isn't usually the local curate. The bishop was prepared to act, but insisted that he needed some confirmation of the stories about Waldron from the local parishioners. This he swiftly received in full measure, to be precise a petition from the parishioners of Burford and Taynton demanding the immediate removal of the curate. The case against Waldron seemed cut and dried, until a most peculiar letter appeared from Great Barrington. Couched in fulsome terms and signed by most of the inhabitants – or at least those who could write – it extolled the virtues of the apparently schizophrenic curate, praising his godliness and good conduct, and giving the general impression that far from removing him there was a general belief that he should be put forward as a candidate for canonization. One of the prime faults of the amateur sinner is overegging the pudding; no one was going to believe a missive so directly opposed to everything that was known about the man. Yet the signatures were obviously genuine; how had he managed it? The bishop decided to investigate.

One name was conspicuous by its absence: a Mr Durnford, one of the tenant farmers of the local landowner, Lord Dynevor. The bishop sent to him to ask why he had not subscribed to the general hero-worship of Waldron, and received the cryptic answer that 'he was sure Lord Dynevor knew Mr Waldron's character too well to require his tenants to set their names to so notorious a falsehood'. Puzzled, the bishop enquired what Lord Dynevor had got to do with it, and was told that the landowner had sent a letter to all his tenant farmers, threatening them with his resentment and displeasure, not to mention the loss of their farms, unless they signed the testimonial to the curate. This came as something of a surprise to the bishop, but not as much as it did to Lord Dynevor. Waldron found himself not only expelled from his curacy, but forbidden by the bishop to exercise any priestly function henceforth, and indeed denounced to the Archbishop of Canterbury.

At this point most people would have accepted defeat and gone quietly.

Waldron went all right, but not defeated; he went with the only key to the vicarage, and threatened to take legal action against anyone entering the premises. De la Bere wrote to the bishop: 'He menaces your Lordship, and threatens to pursue me to my utter ruin and destruction.' Waldron claimed that the vicar owed him £20, and refused to give up the vicarage until he was paid. Desperate to get rid of the man whatever the cost, de la Bere bought him off with a compromise sum, but found that even then he wasn't free. Now that he had money in his pocket, 'the wretch continued at Burford until the whole sum received was spent in riot and intoxication'. Only Waldron's eventual reduction to penury led to his wandering off in search of a new victim.

De la Bere, it will be noticed, was vicar of three parishes long before the notion of united benefices arose. The better class of clergyman would acquire a number of livings around the country, perhaps look after one of them himself, and put curates in to take care of the remainder. This led to one of the evils of the Church in previous centuries: the problem of non-resident vicars and rectors. Occasionally a bishop would address the problem by appointing to a parish on the understanding that the cleric appointed actually resided there to take the services at the church. Of course, as the Revd William Welchman would argue, it all depends what you mean by reside. Welchman wrote from Westcott Barton to the Bishop of Oxford in 1739:

> It is true that I promised to reside here, but I never meant by that expression a total, perpetual, constant residence, which is not only utterly inconsistent with my health, liberty, and the duty I owe to my parish in Northampton, but also to the proper and prudent care I ought in the present distress of bad times to take of my worldly concerns – in a word, such a residence tends directly to my ruin.

Welchman's favourite theme was the way in which the whole world is conspiring to reduce him to beggary, a fate which can only be avoided, it seems, by his being allowed to live in a large town rather than a small village. In particular he objected to Westcott Barton, which he tacitly suggests was not the most exciting place in the universe: 'Mr Bruere declared once to me that he would not reside here for the value of the whole living; how hard must my lot be then, to be doomed to a perpetual residence? I naturally love silence and retirement, but being no sportsman, a constant, solitary, sedentary life my constitution will not bear.' It is difficult to see what he is complaining about, as his letter goes on to indicate that silence and solitude were the last things he was likely to experience in the vicarage: 'I desire that this house may be cleared of the present family placed here by the tenants, for the woman of the house, being a fruitful, teeming woman, bears children so fast, that I am much pestered with the crying of children and their nuisances, and neither I nor my son can brook such inconveniences.'

He had a solution to the problem; if the bishop would only let him return to Northampton, 'in my absence I shall send my son regularly to supply the church, if not every Sunday, yet the greater part of the Sundays'. The son in question was still an undergraduate at Oxford, and hardly competent to act as spiritual leader to a community, but the bishop could manage without a fight and agreed to the deal. This was a bad move, as it confirmed Welchman in his belief that the diocese owed him a living. Five years later he was regretfully forced to withdraw his son's services: 'he hath been lately presented to a small living in Warwickshire distant from Westcott Barton about 22 miles. The circumstances of this living are such that they have necessitated him to enter upon it by entering it himself' – a dreadful fate. This time it was not only Welchman himself but also his son who was staring poverty in the face: 'My son's residence is hindered by his attending his harvest, and the business of farming and grazing, which in these bad times of war threatening beggary and ruin by foreign invasion, by rents decreasing and taxes increasing, may make him as rich as a new shorn sheep.'

This left Westcott Barton without a priest once more, and Welchman was sadly unable to take on personally the responsibilities for which he was being paid: 'My own residence here is prevented by my infirm state of health, which still disables me from the due performance of the public duties of even the smallest cure.' However, once again he had a solution; offload the work on to the minister of the next parish: 'I apply to your lordship to permit Mr Parker, minister of Sandford, to supply Westcott Barton under our present distress. I do not know the gentleman, but I believe him to be a worthy person. . . .' Having thus taken deep care for the welfare of his parishioners, Welchman drifted off into permanent retirement, pausing only to show a little Christian charity towards a poor family in the village: 'A little house that has been in the uninterrupted possession of the church at Barton for above 60 years, has been by violence and a strong hand wrested from me to settle therein a poor family belonging to Steeple Barton. . . .'

Obviously clergy who were failing to do their jobs properly or live up to the standards expected of them were likely to become the subject of episcopal chastisement; occasionally it could happen to those who were getting a little carried away with their priestly functions. John Ford, out in

Piddington, had what might superficially look like a rather odd charge laid against him in 1682: 'We lay against thee, John Ford, that thou didst preach or read a lecture in the parish church or chapel of Piddington on the 15th, 22nd and 29th days of October last past.' The point was that Ford had not been appointed to Piddington parish by the bishop; in fact, to deliver his sermon he had been forced to shout down the vicar. The Civil War period had led to a profusion of dissenting religious sects, which did not disappear at the Restoration but formed their own churches, or occasionally attempted to appropriate those of other people. The attitude of the established Church to these 'interlopers' varied from a rather uncomfortable toleration to outright malevolence.

No sect was more deeply hated than the Quakers. The public perception of them was far from the peace-loving idealists of today; rather they were seen as being close to the ranters, which did them no favours. While other sects might achieve tacit acceptance, the Quakers usually acquired an above average familiarity with the inside of the local gaol – in Oxford, the prison within the castle. Once in they were often quietly forgotten, and a petition survives from five unfortunates who were long-term inmates and wished to have their situation remedied. Note the regrettable way that what begins as a humble plea somehow attains the status of a threat by the end:

It is in our hearts to lay before thee our long imprisonment; some of us are going on into the seventh year, and others are near six years, where we have layen as men buried alive and confined to dwell among wicked and ungodly men, which doth often grieve our spirits. And this imprisonment tendeth not only to bury us alive, but also to the destroying of us and our families, which we hope is far from thy heart to think to do, who are men of peace and seek to live so with all men, and have never acted any thing against the King, thyself, nor any other unto this very day; neither dare we to deny the Lord, nor his truth made manifest unto us, whatever thee or any other shall have power to inflict upon us, who know the day to be come that Christ spoke of, that the true worshippers must worship God in spirit and truth, for which truth we do suffer and are kept in bonds to this very day, and for no injury or wrong done to any man, as God is our witness, unto whom all of us must give an account. So it is the desire of us who are and have been long prisoners and sufferers, that thee wouldst seriously weigh and consider of this our condition, to set at liberty the poor, afflicted and long oppressed, *whilst thee had power and time given thee to do the thing*. . . .

Sometimes it was safer for the Quakers to be in gaol. Even before the Restoration the Puritans were active in attacking their meetings; the house of Richard Betteris in New Inn Hall Street was a favourite target, particularly of the scholars of St John's College, who had already amused themselves by tying up two Quaker women and throwing them in a pond. They smashed Betteris' windows, broke up the meetings with squibs and gunpowder, burst in yelling, 'Give us beer and tobacco!', and when they got the beer poured it down the necks of the congregation. Yet there were a few adherents of the established Church who tried to show some charity towards those of whom they disapproved. Richard Baylis, vice-chancellor of the university, was expected to proceed against Quakers wherever they were found, and in May 1662 he was informed that a huge congregation was once again gathered in their New Inn Hall Street haunt. Reluctantly he made his way down there to deal with them:

> I fairly besought them to depart; they absolutely refused. I read the Act unto them, newly published for the suppression of such conventicles, and added another short, sharp lecture unto it, that I would presently put the same into severe execution. The threat no whit moved them but to high terms of scorn, and vaunts that neither prison or gallows should make them change their resolution. I fell to entreaty and persuasion that they would have pity upon themselves and quietly depart; all in vain. Thus provoked to just execution according to the Act, yet foolish pity prevailed against my judgement and overcame me to dispense, where the law did not warrant me. In fine, with some show of force I made a shift to clear the room and dissolve the congregation, and to carry my old prisoner Bettris to Boccardo.

By the 1680s another noted Oxfordshire figure was adopting the velvet glove approach to religious dissenters. Bishop John Fell – now remembered principally as the subject of the quatrain 'I do not love thee, Dr Fell' – took the rational view that few fanatics or extremists were ever moved by threats or violence. Instead he instructed his clergy to dispute with the dissenters in their parishes, to discover their quarrel with the Church and thus perhaps persuade them back into the fold. Many of his clergy seemed to have some difficulty grasping this approach. He was their bishop, however, and orders are orders. Out they went to talk with men and women they patently hated. Edward Tyrer in Clanfield reported the following:

> I asked a Quaker why he would not come to Church. 'I'll tell thee,' says he, 'why I can't come to thy church. I have set my hand to the

plough and I can't look back.' Another told me the Church of England has erred from the truth that is in Christ Jesus, therefore they had separated themselves as a holy and pure people, as Enotch, Enotch (for so he notched the word) was a perfect man and walked with God, with a great deal of canting rabble – the pride and insolence of these filthy dreamers is intolerable.

Over in Drayton, Adam Morton showed a most unChristian attitude towards his erring parishioners:

Two families are sectarists; the one are called Anabaptists, the other Quakers. I have discoursed with them, and although they can say little or nothing for their opinions, yet they are wilful. We are not like to be long troubled with them, for Gilkes, the Anabaptist, hath an incurable disease which will shortly put an end to his life, and Millers, the Quaker, for not paying his landlord's rent, is to hold his farm but one year more. . . .

It would hardly be surprising if the dissenters began to fight back. Up in Banbury, earlier in the century, they did precisely that. Banbury was well known as a stronghold of Puritanism – not the most tactful place to have statues of saints in niches around the outside of the church. One morning when these statues were found littering the flagstones at the foot of the church, smashed or defaced, the Church authorities were at pains to point out that they were simply figures of men, and not in any way intended to be religious images, saying 'the statues were accounted only as ornaments of the parish church, without any superstition or idolatry growing or practised thereby'. The fact remained that they had been fixed to the walls of the church with iron bands or with lime and mortar, and were quite a distance from the ground, so someone must have gone to considerable trouble to destroy them. In an attempt to find out who, the Church authorities turned into the first Oxfordshire detectives, and were a credit to their newly invented profession. What they needed was someone with motive, means and opportunity.

Finding a motive was not difficult; any Puritan in Banbury would have been delighted to smash the relics of Popish practices. In that community this did not narrow the field appreciably. Nevertheless, the authorities started to look carefully at the backgrounds of some suspicious figures. In the days following the event Agnes Kerwood was heard speaking 'concerning the pulling down of the statues, and did constantly say or affirm that it was well done'. That put her high on the list of suspects for a start, so our detectives investigated her contacts, and found 'that she doth know or credibly believe that the wife of one Pitts hath stood excommunicated for the space of this year and a half last past, but in contempt of that high censure she hath received her to her house and hath accompanied or guided her to the church of Banbury at the time of sermon there and continued in her company there during the sermon'. That someone is a known frequenter of the company of villains doesn't constitute proof of guilt, so what more practical evidence was there?

Anyone could have had access to a crowbar, but what about the ladder to reach the statues in the first place? Henry Hollihead came under suspicion here. About the very time the statues were smashed, he was round at Thomas Kimbell's house borrowing precisely that useful item. Again, this was not conclusive proof, but there weren't too many ladders around in Banbury at that time, and one has to admit it looks like an odd coincidence. A definite suspicion was forming around a specific group of local Puritans, but something more solid was needed. The authorities found it in the form of the third item in the classic mystery trio: opportunity.

The big mistake which the guilty parties made was in not leaving well alone. They had heaved the statues down from the church, expecting them to smash into fragments on the flags below. Unfortunately one of them had failed to do so; it remained whole, if a little chipped around the edges. Any sensible villain would have shrugged his shoulders and let it go at that, but this crowd were fanatics, unable to rest until every statue had been destroyed. This led them to their downfall.

The remaining statue, and the fragments of its companions, had been gathered together by the churchwardens and sidesmen of Banbury parish, and placed for safekeeping in a room in the church. One morning they were horrified to find that someone had been in the room overnight, and 'by some engine or other means' had broken the remaining statue in two. Yet the locks of the church doors had not been tampered with. Suddenly something became obvious; very few people had the opportunity to get into that room, and whoever it was had to be an official of the church. The authorities investigated, and very soon came to a conclusion: 'Robert Benbow has for these three years last past been the sexton of the parish church of Banbury, and by virtue of that place has had during all the aforesaid time the custody of the keys, doors and passages of the church, so that no persons might come into the church without privity or knowledge'. No one else could have had access; it was an open and shut case. The three malefactors and sundry confederates were brought before the courts and indicted in due process of justice, and the Church authorities could congratulate themselves on a brilliant and successful investigation. Of course they were slightly helped by something which appears as a throwaway tailpiece in the court proceedings: that there has been and still is 'a public voice and fame' of the defendants' guilt throughout Banbury and the surrounding parishes.

Clergymen could have problems with their own Church superiors, they could have problems with those who held a not entirely compatible faith, but they could also have considerable problems with lay rectors. The dissolution of the monasteries and the parcelling out of former monastic estates to wealthy individuals had led to the right of presenting a clergyman to a living ending up with the oddest people or institutions. Oxford colleges were particularly prone to end up with the right, as many of them had former Church lands in their endowments. This gave a lay body rather more control over individual clergymen than the clergymen thought was desirable.

On 7 November 1819 Bartley Lee, the curate of Combe, wrote to his friend Mr Richardson of Covent Garden: 'I should esteem it a great favour if you would try to look over the will of the late Dr Hutchins, who died Rector of Lincoln College, and collect what information you can from it concerning this curacy.' His friend did as requested, and replied: 'to me it appears there is great power lodged with the rector and fellows of Lincoln'. The enquiry was an interesting piece of prescience on Lee's part, because exactly one year later Dr Tatham, the then Rector of Lincoln, informed the curate that his services were no longer required and that he was being replaced by a certain Charles Rose.

Exactly why Tatham wanted to get rid of Lee remains obscure. During subsequent events Tatham's supporters talk about 'just and sufficient reason' for his actions, Lee's of 'the private malevolence' of Tatham and his wife. The local paper, which *may* be less biased, reported that 'some complaint was made by a number of the inhabitants of Combe to Dr Tatham against Mr Lee', but still carefully avoids saying what the complaint actually was. If some of the parishioners were opposed to Lee, they kept well out of the way during what happened next.

Charles Rose turned up bright and early on the Sunday to take service in his new church, only to find the path to the church door blocked. To be precise it was blocked by Thomas Bumpus, the churchwarden; Lee arrived, took the service, and announced that he was not going anywhere but would continue as curate of Combe. He then produced a lock which he put on the door of the pulpit, pocketed the key and left. This left Rose in a bit of a quandary, which he solved the only way possible; he went back to Lincoln College and informed Dr Tatham that there seemed to be some doubt about who exactly was the curate of Combe.

In Tatham's mind there was no doubt whatsoever, and he determined to make the point to Lee as forcibly as possible. He took the curate to court, but during an unnecessarily protracted case Lee and his friends suffered two misfortunes which swung popular sympathy firmly on to their side. To start with, someone comprehensively vandalized Thomas Bumpus' orchard, which may have been pure coincidence but looked awfully like petty spite on the part of the Tatham party. Working on the conspiracy theory, one might be tempted to assume that Lee organized it in order to discredit his opponents, but he was hardly likely to have arranged the second misfortune: his own wife fell ill and died. Lee immediately claimed that her illness had been caused by the strain of being persecuted by Tatham and his friends, and made the claim plausible enough for it to be believed by many.

Yet the court was there to determine a point of law, not to have its sympathies engaged; it finally ruled that Tatham had the right to throw Lee out of the church and churchyard. The Tatham party was jubilant, but its celebrations were to be shortlived. Lee had seen it coming, and had a ploy in reserve which Tatham had not been expecting. Under the recent Act of Parliament regulating curacies, he claimed that whatever Tatham's rights might be over presentation to the living, he had no rights over the parsonage house, and that therefore he, Lee, could live there for as long as he pleased. He won.

It may have been this which made Tatham see red and make his first serious tactical error. In order to demonstrate to the inhabitants of Combe that he had achieved his ends, and that the miserable wretch who was continuing to live comfortably in the parsonage house had actually lost, appearances notwithstanding, he decided to take over the church and conduct a service there in person. Subsequently, when justifications were being required, he claimed that dropping in to take a service in a small, obscure country church was a perfectly natural thing for the Rector of Lincoln College to do, and was in no way intended as a confrontation. Some doubt was cast on this statement by the fact that he arrived at Combe with a hefty bodyguard consisting of the Duke of Marlborough's gamekeepers. But the Duke of Marlborough simply didn't have enough gamekeepers to match the mob, four or five hundred strong, who had occupied the churchyard and, under the leadership of Lee and Lord Charles Churchill (which must have been particularly galling for the Duke), were chanting 'No Tatham! Lee for ever!'

Having got into the habit of making tactical errors, Tatham put in some solid practice with a few more. First he tried to force his way through the churchyard. This proved to be a bad move, and he desisted. Next he realized that some of his friends had managed to hold the door by the church porch for him and he headed towards it. This drew the attention of the mob to the fact, and they dealt with the friends accordingly. One of them was the local constable, Austin, who was effectively beaten up, while one of his colleagues was thrown over a gravestone. Feeling that this showed a lack of respect towards the forces of law and order, Austin later took certain members of the mob to court on a charge of assaulting him in the course of his duty; to his chagrin the court threw the case out on the grounds that whatever it was Austin thought he was doing, it certainly wasn't his duty. Lee himself then attempted to get into the church to perform the service, only to find that some of Tatham's men had sneaked in the previous evening and barred the door. This was no problem for a man with a large mob at his fingertips; he called them over and they broke it down for him. The service then proceeded.

Lee, Lord Charles Churchill and several of the strong-arm men ended up in court on a charge of riot; three of the strong-arm men were sent down, but the two principals walked away without a stain on their characters. This was particularly annoying for Tatham, as Churchill had been heard quite clearly yelling 'Do your duty – pull them out!' while the mob were laying into Tatham's bodyguard. All of this probably goes to show that it's the poor that get the blame, particularly in cases where embarrassingly eminent personages are involved. Tatham did get his way at last; Lee could not continue to hold the church against a court order, and he left, to be replaced by Charles Rose.

There were, however, two interesting postscripts to the affair. First, a letter appeared in the *Oxford Journal* shortly after, signed by 105 parishioners of Combe, thanking Tatham for getting rid of Lee. On investigation, only four of the 105 turned out to be real people. In view of which, the second postscript takes on the aspect of poetic justice. Rose proved to be a first-rate curate. Not only was he a devout man and a powerful spiritual leader, he was also deeply concerned about social problems and particularly the welfare of the poor; indeed he was quite indefatigable at forcing the farmers to contribute handsomely to their assistance. A member of the Tatham party was heard to grumble: 'We might as well have kept Mr Lee!'

Whatever the long-lost rights and wrongs of the affair, Lee undeniably had courage to stand up to the Rector of Lincoln. Certain clergy of Oxfordshire seem to have lacked the courage to stand up to their own parishioners even to carry out their legal functions, although that may say more about the parishioners than the priest. Each year the clergy were expected to bring to the bishop their formal answers to a list of questions on their church and parish, circulated by the bishop a week or two earlier. Thomas Leigh of Lower Heyford did not bring his 1738 answers; instead he sent them by a circuitous route, with a covering letter:

My Lord – On Saturday last I received your Lordship's queries and beg leave by this way to transmit my answer to them; for I am apprehensive that if I deliver them at Bicester, my parishioners may be suspicious that I have given some informations against them. This I would willingly prevent, being sensible it will lessen that influence which I wish and pray I may always have over them. I have acquainted my parish with all the things which I complain of to your Lordship, and begged of them that they might be reformed, but all my entreaties, or even threats, to acquaint the Ordinary with it have been to no purpose. I believe, my Lord, it is not a disregard to decency, but poverty is the occasion of those things; every penny comes with extreme difficulty from them, and I verily think there are very few poorer parishes in your Lordship's diocese. . . .

He may well have been right, judging by the subsequent list, which runs systematically through the fabric and contents of the church and finds fault with every item, down to the condition of the road outside. On the other hand, he may have had a set of locals like those encountered a hundred years earlier by Lawrence Griffith, when he arrived to become curate of Holwell. Griffith needed somewhere to stay when he arrived in the area, and he tried the nearest town of any size, Burford. While in the ale house of Robert Aston discussing terms, he accepted the invitation of the regulars to have a drink with them. One drink led to another, and finally Aston suggested that it was time to settle up. It was at this point that Griffith discovered who had been standing the rounds, something he had never considered to be one of the duties of a new incumbent. Apart from the sheer injustice of the situation, there was also the minor inconvenience that he had no money on him. He informed the company of this, and the situation ceased to be unjust and became ugly instead.

The locals were aggrieved, and showed it: 'Forest and Simon Partridge of Burford pulled off his coat, proffering to lend him money on the same, then William Drewett pulled off his boot and beat him with it.' In fact, things seem to have got out of hand: 'Aston, Crofts and Drewett in a violent, contemptuous and scornful manner, put Griffith into a tub or vessel and bid him preach, and crossed his face with a coal or some such black thing.' Eventually Griffith escaped, but it was hardly an auspicious start to his curacy; he got his revenge in court – the Church courts liked their clergy to be treated with the proper degree of respect – but he must have wondered what his flock were likely to do if they disapproved of one of his sermons.

If a clergyman has to have enemies in the parish, it is difficult to say whether quality or quantity is more dangerous. Some, like James Palmer,

The much unloved Dr Fell, nevertheless one of the most impressive bishops of Oxford diocese (*Oxfordshire Archives*)

Bishop Samuel – 'Soapy Sam' – Wilberforce, the master politician of Oxford diocese in the nineteenth century (*Oxfordshire Archives*)

the curate of Headington in 1805, find themselves caught between both. He wrote to the Bishop of Oxford, giving a free and frank description of the various personalities involved in a dispute which had broken out there, so free and frank that he urged the bishop to destroy the letter when read. There is a moral in this; I wish I had a nominal sum of money for every letter I have seen preserved in an archive repository which urges the recipient to destroy it after reading it through. The request is almost a guarantee that great care will be taken to preserve it, and fortunately in this case; how else would we have such a delightfully candid snapshot of life in the parish?

> Mr Whorwood, the lay rector, is a man who from having lived a very debauched life and having been to Germany [Palmer seems to feel the two things go together], that hot-bed of modern infidelity and mental quackery, has imbibed notions so contrary to all religion and everything resembling it that he does not scruple to call it priestcraft, and to talk and argue in such a way that I will not stain my paper, or offend your Lordship, by repeating his ideas, which seem to have been raked together from all the heresies which were ever broached. To add to his misfortunes, he has lately married a woman considerably his inferior in point of family, whose upstart pride has disgusted several friends who still adhere to him. His situation, in short, is such that the strictest attention to his behaviour and conduct for twelve or fourteen years to come will scarcely be sufficient to gain him that respect which his birth and station in life entitle him to.
>
> His brother, the vicar, is in a state of such dependence on him that he cannot differ from him materially without danger of starvation.
>
> Mr Lock, whose improper conduct has made no inconsiderable disturbance in this parish, is a person in whose estimation the possession of money is a compensation for the absence of almost everything else [human nature has changed little in two hundred years], and although Mr Whorwood *to my certain knowledge* most heartily despises him, yet he finds it convenient to show him some civilities and attentions, for it is said that he has borrowed money of him. Mr Lock would not be so much disliked as he is, if he did not permit his wife, who is a busy, meddling woman, to interfere as much as she does in everything in which he is concerned. He suffers her to make a fool of him, therefore he is a fool.

This is straight out of a classic detective story; the web of tensions and linkages is set up; now it only remains to discover who the victim is.

Actually the victim was the population of Headington Quarry, and the villain Mr Lock. The enclosure award of 1801 gave him a parcel of land across which ran the old footpath from Quarry to Headington used to bring coffins to the parish church. He built a wall across it. The next funeral to come along put the coffin down, demolished the wall, picked the coffin up again and continued on its way. Lock rebuilt the wall. The next funeral broke it down again. He rebuilt it. They demolished it. He took three of the men involved to court, and tried to enlist Palmer's help to persuade the Quarry inhabitants to use an alternative route. Palmer was not disposed to give it:

> The inhabitants of Quarry think themselves aggrieved in being deprived of this path, and seem to lay a great stress on its having been a funeral path time immemorial; and indeed it does appear hard that for the accommodation of one upstart fellow, the inhabitants of a whole hamlet should be distressed. As the new path is near 250 yards further about, and as it appeared to me not only absurd but a kind of insult against the Church itself, I flatly refused him. I am not to be dazzled by any man's wealth, and can very clearly see the dangerous tendency of that blind adoration paid to riches, which is so prevalent at the present time.

Thus the high-principled clergyman stood up for his parishioners against the encroaching parvenu; they repaid him by stabbing him in the back: 'the inhabitants of Quarry now say that as they are to be deprived of their funeral path, they will not come to Church at all, but intend to have a Methodist preacher come to them'. Lock was immovable, backed by a wife who was not prepared to lose face. Whorwood hated Lock, but was financially bound to him, and was not going to take the risk of upsetting him for the sake of a man whose religion he despised. The vicar was under Whorwood's control. Palmer suddenly found he had been playing a game of politics well out of his depth. His final letter to the bishop was a bitter, baffled resignation. 'The purse-proud sons of wealth generally combine together,' he wrote. The bishop didn't lift a finger for him either.

If it seems to be taking principle to absurd lengths to resign from a job, with no immediate future prospects for yourself, your sick wife, and two young children, all on account of a minor footpath diversion, bear in mind that Oxfordshire has a rich tradition of eccentric or plain erratic churchmen.

As early as the 1620s, Bishop Corbett of Oxford had a widespread reputation for *lèse-majesté*. On one market day he and some of his ecclesiastical companions were at the tavern by the cross in Abingdon. A ballad hawker there was complaining loudly that he had no custom; no one would buy his songs. Dr Corbett promptly removed his gown and borrowed the hawker's leather jacket, then went out into the market-place and started up a brisk trade, using his powerful voice trained in intoning the services to sing various samples of his wares across the square. The hawker reportedly had one of his best days for a long time. Examples of his wit were noted down in various writings of the time, and if, like some much-quoted Thomas Beecham stories, they seem less than rib-tickling, consider how astonishing it was for a bishop's one-liners to be considered worth noting down at all. On one occasion, as he was conducting a confirmation in a country parish, the crowd pressed rather too close, and Corbett cried 'Be off there, or I'll confirm you all with my staff!' On another, laying his hand in blessing on the head of a bald man, he turned to his curate and said, 'Some dust here, Lushington, to keep my hand from slipping.' No? Well, perhaps the Oxfordshire eccentrics are more endearing when they're not trying to be.

Matthew Griffith, the incumbent of Bladon at the time of the Civil War, made no attempt to be endearing to anyone, least of all the Parliamentarian forces. He was a staunch Royalist who had been given his first living by Charles I and didn't forget it; imprisoned in 1642, he got away and fought for the king in the unsuccessful defence of Basing House. Evidently a tactless attitude towards Cromwell's supporters ran in the family; when Basing House fell the Parliamentarians were prepared to treat the losers with courtesy, but they had reckoned without Griffith's daughter. She set up such a relentless barrage of insults at them that one soldier finally lost his temper and killed her. The living of Bladon was Charles II's gift to the aging clergyman after the Restoration, but Griffith found that life just wasn't the same without the Roundheads to shoot at and insult. As a compensation he set to work on his congregation, haranguing them in fine style from the pulpit, until, perhaps to their relief, he burst a blood vessel during one of his most passionate attacks and fell down dead at their feet.

Edward Bagshaw of Ambrosden, on the other hand, was thrown out of his living in 1662 having been on the other side. This came as no surprise to anyone who knew him. He had got into the habit of bloody-mindedness early, when at Christ Church — being accused of insolence to the Vice-Chancellor in a dispute over the abolition of hoods and caps. After this promising start he became Second Master of Westminster School, where the headmaster accused him of wearing his hat in church and 'taking a strange delight in whipping'. The Royalists who removed him from Ambrosden had no wish to be vindictive, and informed him that if he would live quietly in the country for a year to allow old wounds to heal, they would give him preferment. The strain was too much for him; within a few months he was in gaol for refusing to take the oath of allegiance, and he died while still on parole.

Eccentric incumbents can be entertaining to outsiders, but they are apt to be something of a strain for those who have to work with them. John Gould was appointed Rector of Beaconsfield in 1816, at the age of thirty-six. Unfortunately he was still there forty years later, but doing very little of the work, having through age and indolence degenerated into a front man for the activities of his daughter, the aptly named Hussey. One of Hussey's little quirks was that she disliked curates, not, one suspects, because she once had an unhappy liaison with one, but because they would insist on wanting to do some of the work around the parish. Matters came to a head when a certain Mr Major was appointed curate and refused to be dictated to. Gould was prevailed upon by his daughter to complain to the bishop. The bishop in question was Wilberforce, who wrote down the sequel in one of his memoranda books:

12 March 1856, old Gould quarrels with Major, because, quotha, he will not bow down to Hussey Gould. June 1858, Mr Gould writes that he wishes to part with Major. I remonstrate. Gould asks for an interview. He comes with daughter Hussey, who complains a long-winded complaint of ill will, mischief, etc, while old Gould sits by and reads my papers! She eloquent . . . Told Hussey I would enquire. Archdeacon reports favourably to Major, and with much difficulty I rearrange their relations amicably.

However, the dispute broke out again in 1862, and Major offered to resign. Wilberforce declined to accept, and instead sent a letter which must have caused the curate to start chewing the carpet:

Only let me urge upon you whilst you keep the curacy to be more than ever on your guard to make your whole conduct both to the rector and all his family as conciliatory as possible; not only making allowance for that natural irritableness of old age, but remembering that he has many causes of annoyance, and that your continuance in the parish must be disturbing to his temper. I do not doubt your diligence in work. But writing to you as your bishop, I cannot forbear asking you to consider whether your ministry is as full as it should be of all the life and unction of Christ's divine gospel of reconciliation and love.

Major might well have responded by enquiring where precisely Christ exempted elderly rectors from that aspect of His gospel.

It is sometimes difficult to say where mere eccentricity starts sliding into something a little more sinister. Take the case of Robert Lumblee Kening, curate of Somerton in the late eighteenth century. Kening was up to date with the latest political principles and ideas; indeed, he even started propounding them from the pulpit at regular intervals. Today most people accept this aspect of the Church's ministry, but the problem with Kening was that the principles he was advocating were those of the French Revolution, and his country congregation was a little taken aback to hear the removal of the king and a mass dispatch of the British aristocracy urged by their clergyman. The village schoolmaster left one of his sermons muttering, 'Such a fellow ought to be pulled out of the pulpit.' When Kening started to put into practice some of the less seemly side-effects of the revolution the bishop was inclined to agree, and served him with an inhibition for gross immorality. Kening took advantage of his unexpected leisure time to visit the Continent and see the revolution in action, but rather sadly he returned to Somerton, broken in health and impoverished, and died in the loft over his own former stables.

On more than one occasion it was a desire to improve their standing in the parish which led members of the clergy into dubious ways. John Mavor had already acquired a reputation before taking on the living of Forest Hill in the middle of the nineteenth century. While at Lincoln College he featured regularly in the common room betting book, where he appears to be the prototype of Runyon's Sky Masterson – he would lay odds on anything. Unfortunately for his subsequent career, his most unsuccessful bet was that he could build a massive rectory at Forest Hill on an inadequate stipend. First he had to sell off his books to meet his debts, followed by his furniture, and eventually his own lawyer, tired of the unpaid bills, had him imprisoned. He ended his life writing remarkably unsuccessful begging letters to the Bishop of Lincoln.

Even Mavor was not as extravagant as Heathcote Brooks. Brooks was the Rector of Great Rollright, a parish which had already received a good deal of attention from its incumbents. Brasenose College had granted loans for improvements to Church property and lands in 1783, again in 1813, and once more in 1822. Brooks was not impressed. He found the seventeenth-century rectory far too cramped and pokey for his needs and proceeded to demolish it, providing in its place a building which appeared to be alive, since far from following any pre-ordained building plan it grew at the whim of its creator. The hall and staircase would have been more at home in a manor house; the cellars were enormous. Contemporary accounts tell of the rector appearing at regular intervals during construction with cries of 'Give me air! Give me space! Enlarge it here! Enlarge it there!' The only drawback to this building programme was a complete absence of money to pay for it. As time drew on, Brooks' creditors became more insistent in their demands to be paid, and began to congregate in the road outside to lobby him. Eventually the only way he could get to the church to conduct services on Sundays was through the vegetable patch. Finally, in 1851, after two years of building work, he reached the church by his usual route, entered the pulpit, and announced that his text for the day was 'Forgive us our debts as we forgive our debtors'. He then retired from the pulpit and entered the vestry. After a few minutes his congregation grew restless and went to look for him. He wasn't there. They never saw him again.

At least Mavor and Brooks were attempting to increase the prestige of the clergy, even if they succeeded in doing the reverse. Some clerics appear to have been engaging in a single-minded attempt to discredit the entire calling. Francis Davis, Vicar of Spelsbury in the late seventeenth century, was a case in point. It was reported to the bishop that his behaviour was not up to standard, and at the annual visitation in 1679 he was told to mend his ways. He responded by getting worse. He was instructed, not only by the bishop but also by the canons of the Church of England, to read the litany in his church on Wednesdays and Sundays; he never got round to it. All clergy were enjoined 'not to resort to taverns and alehouses' – Davis was seldom found anywhere else – and 'neither shall they play at cards, dice or tables or any other unlawful games' – Davis conducted himself like the man who broke the bank at Monte Carlo. When he had been drinking and the cards went against him, he was not beyond having a stand-up fight with one of his parishioners. This sort of lifestyle needed money, a lot more than his stipend provided, but Davis found a simple way of augmenting his income. Although it was laid down that 'no minister shall refuse to bury a corpse, if the deceased was not denounced excommunicate', Davis found that grieving relatives with the body of a loved one on their hands were in a very bad bargaining position if he decided not to read the funeral service. He took to demanding an impromptu and illegal fee of 10s. (50p) for doing so, until on 20 August 1679 one Robert Souch refused to pay up and the corpse was buried without the last rites. This was the last straw, and Davis was hauled up to answer for his conduct in the bishop's court.

Strangely enough, funerals often seem to bring out the worst in churchmen who are too fond of the bottle. Perhaps it's because of the innate solemnity of the occasion. The Vicar of St Peter-le-Bailey, Oxford, was long suffering over his sexton, but eventually, in June 1828, found himself obliged to complain to the vestry meeting:

Gentlemen – It is with extreme reluctance that I at length complain to you of the repeated ill conduct of the sexton (King) in appearing at church in a state of intoxication, and I am now particularly induced to do so by the very indecent and unfeeling behaviour of which he was guilty at a funeral on Saturday evening last. Intoxication had so completely overpowered him, that it was only by the mourners who stood near that he was prevented from falling into the grave, and I regret to say that the corpse was interred in a manner very revolting to the feelings of every bystander, and more particularly to the attendant relatives. I am sure you will adopt such measures as may prevent a recurrence of an enormity so impious and detestable.

The sexton grovelled, and was pardoned with the loss of three months' salary. Perhaps the vestry was grateful that it was only the sexton. Down the road in Beckley a few years earlier, the curate, Richardson Wood, was acting in a way which made Sexton King look like a model of propriety. When the bishop finally took him in hand there were twenty-one charges laid against him, starting with drunkenness and progressing from there:

Towards the end of 1796, you became addicted to excessive drinking of spiritous and other strong liquors and have since paid so little regard to your sacred function as to give yourself up to habitual intoxication.

The first result of this was a tendency to forget services, which was bad enough on Sundays but eventually spread. On Christmas Day 1799 he failed to show up for service, and after a diligent search was found dead drunk in the Crown and Thistle, Headington. In some ways this was preferable to his attendance. True to type he was a particularly embarrassing addition to funeral parties. At the burial of Mary Taylor of Horton, in 1800, he actually failed to get through the service. In an attempt to prevent a recurrence of this at the funeral of a member of the Sedwell family, his parishioners went looking for him in the pub well before time, and hauled him off to the house of the Parish Clerk, William Carr, to sober up. Unfortunately he was already too far gone, and Carr had to dash over to John Sedwell's house and beg him not to bring the corpse along to church until word was sent that the priest was in a fit state to deal with it. Sedwell was a long-standing parishioner and could take this with a resigned sigh; it wasn't quite so easy when the bereaved family came from outside the parish. Miss Susanna Oxley of Gloucester was visiting the Ledwell family of Beckley Park when she took sick and died; her funeral caught the curate literally with his pants down:

You attended, but in such a state of extreme intoxication as to appear whilst performing – or rather whilst attempting to perform – the burial service with the flap of your breeches down and your stockings hanging about your heels, and it was with the utmost difficulty that you could get through the same.

Apparently his behaviour was the same at baptisms. Ralph Butler, one of his parishioners, was nearly very lucky; Wood almost failed to make it to the church for the service:

In your way thither, being very much intoxicated from drinking to excess of strong liquors, you fell into a brook near Headington Wick, and would have been drowned if you had not been dragged out by two men who were luckily passing by at the time.

Not that there was always very much proof of whether Wood had made it to the church or not. When he wasn't too drunk to read the service he was generally too drunk to remember to fill in the registers afterwards. Unfortunately Wood had precisely that effect on some of his parishioners which every clergyman wishes he might have; they profited by his example. Most of the local labourers gave up going to church, and instead were found in the pub during the time of divine service. When accused of impiety, they replied that they were just as good as the parson. Come to that, they probably had a better chance of seeing the parson than their fellows who spent Sunday morning in the parish church.

Wood, however, was a pale reflection of his great predecessor, John Martin, the Rector of Begbroke in the mid-seventeenth century. Martin was a drunkard with the best of them, not even letting up during the annual visitation, when it was said of him:

that he is a common drunkard, and in particular was so far gone in drink at a visitation at Woodstock at the house of George Reeves that he slept at the table where he sat before he did remove, not remembering what he said before, as he did afterwards acknowledge.

He had been warned about this sort of behaviour before, without taking the slightest notice:

Thou hast been admonished to keep home and not to ramble abroad, and to behave thyself civilly, yet thou hast upon slight or no occasion at all frequented markets and public places of meeting, tippling and debauching thyself in alehouses, unto the scandal and reproach of the ministerial function.

When under the influence, Martin was apt to use a breadth of vocabulary not generally associated with men of the cloth, including the oath 'God damn me!', which at that time was the equivalent of a present-day clergyman reeling around his parish yelling four letter obscenities at passers-by. Not surprisingly the drinking had an effect on his services:

Thou didst once at least, at Evening Prayer, so much mistake thyself by reason of drink that thou didst read the Litany,

and even when he was reasonably sober, he seemed to have some difficulty in coping with both of the churches in his care:

Thou dost officiate at two places or parish churches, by reason of which thou keepest such unseasonable hours at Begbroke, that the parishioners or part of them cannot come time enough in the morning, and in the evening it has been so late before thou camest to officiate there, that one could scarcely see any word or letter in the book, except those that sit by the windows.

Certain of the parishioners took a dim view of this, and made their opinions known to the rector. Given Martin's character flaws, this may not have been such a good idea. When he had neglected the reading of prayers one morning he was approached by Mrs Nott, who asked him 'whether we should have no prayers today?', to which he replied in a very slighting manner 'God judge me, what Holy day is it today?', adding that there was time enough to serve God yet. The incident seems to have sparked off a feud between the rector and the Nott family. Martin, who was already rather careless about where he exercised his horse, took to riding over Nott's crops, bringing friends with him to increase the damage:

Thou didst usually ride over thy parish churchyard, and bring company with thee, and leap or go over the wall into Mr Charles Nott's ground with thy horse, others following thee.

He also joined forces with the local bad lot, Sir Thomas Spencer, who had his own feud on with Nott:

Since thou wast admonished not to ride abroad with Sir Thomas Spencer, thou didst ride up with him, with several others in the company, to Mr Nott's gate, at which time Sir Thomas vented forth many oaths and ill language towards Mr Nott, and 'tis believed thou wast not ignorant of his purpose and intent to quarrel with Mr Nott.

The tales of John Martin are full of him riding hither and thither, but he doesn't seem to have been very good at it:

Once, riding over Kidlington Green, and having drunk more than became thy office, thou didst fall in a ditch, and being helped out by one then present thou didst swear 'God judge me, I'll leap my mare over!', and in endeavouring thou fellest in again.

Stabling horses and heavy drinking ate up the money. Martin, like Davis after him, needed to augment his income, but Martin was a man of wider vision. Davis was content with the odd ten shillings from funeral parties, but Martin went into the timber business in a big way. He sold off the wood from the Church glebe land, which he had no right to do, and when asked to explain his conduct replied in an endearingly naïve way that he wanted the money.

In matters of sexual morality Martin seems to have been far from naïve. In fact he was acting as the go-between in an affair between a married man and a married woman. When he was finally brought to court for it the names of the parties were carefully supressed, rather in the manner of the protection given to supergrasses today. He had certainly been carrying letters between them 'where there was but too much reason to suspect the ends to be dishonourable', and where the man's letters failed to have the desired effect, brought his own arguments to bear:

Thou wast for an hour or thereabouts one Sunday in an afternoon in private discourse with that married woman, whom thou didst seldom a day in a week omit speaking with once or twice, and some part of thy language being overheard, it was understood to be the persuading of the married woman to go and live at the married man's house, and not to regard what his wife should say.

Eventually he seems to have achieved his ends, as he brought the man to the house of a gentleman where the married woman was, and sent them upstairs to a chamber together; when a maidservant in the house tried to go up, he 'did clap to a door at the foot of the stairs and said she must not go up there'. While performing these little services for his parishioners he did not neglect his own needs:

> Upon many Sundays after prayers was done, there being at thy house one footboy or other servant of Sir Thomas Spencer's of Yarnton, thou didst ride away with him towards Hanborough, where is a house of no good fame.

Martin seems to have been getting away with this sort of behaviour for a considerable time before he made the fatal mistake which brought him before the bishop. Ironically it was a disaster some 60 miles away which set the chain of events in motion. In the early hours of Sunday 2 September 1666 fire broke out in a bakehouse in Pudding Lane, London. Within hours it was evident that this was no minor conflagration, and four days later the Great Fire of London had destroyed over 500 acres of the city. Briefs were sent out to parishes across the country to collect money for the relief of the victims. After a while the Bishop of Oxford noticed that he had no record of money being sent in from Begbroke, and he sent his mandatory out to see what had happened. As usual Martin was drunk, and when the mandatory asked him for a certificate of the money collected, reacted in a most unexpected manner:

> Thou didst fall a railing upon the mandatory, calling him rogue and dog, and that he was a dog to all the parsons, and speaking very irreverently of thy Bishop. Thou didst say the Bishop was a fool to employ such a knave. Then thou didst strike the said mandatory several times upon his head with thy cudgel and told him, 'There's a certificate for you!' And the mandatory then entreating thee to be civil, and saying that he was sorry to see thee in that condition and telling thee that thou wouldst be sorry for it when thou wast sober, thou replydest 'God damn me, I will not!', and then repeating more blows upon him, thou bidst him go tell my Lord Bishop what thou hadst done.

He did. The bishop requested an early interview with Martin and took him before the ecclesiastical court. Martin claimed that the business with the mandatory had been exaggerated out of all proportion, that he had been provoked by his visitor's calling him 'Drunken priest', and his refusal to accept the quittance which Martin had proffered as genuine, and anyway he had only struck the mandatory's hat. He was still left with the other embarrassing accusations of drunkenness and general immorality, which were much more difficult to talk his way out of. He was forced to do penance, yet he survived as rector, eventually dying in harness many years later. The ways of the Church courts could be strange.

Of course penance was none too pleasant a punishment. It was humiliating to say the least, to parade in a white gown asking pardon of those offended; when imposed for suspected heretical opinions it could be terrifying both for the victim and for those to whom he was set up as a warning. On the occasion of Mr Malary's recantation of his beliefs in the church of St Mary the Virgin, Oxford, in 1541, it became terrifying for all present, due to an astonishing spread of mass hysteria. The story is told by Fox:

There was one Mr Malary, master of arts in Cambridge, who for certain opinions was convened before the bishops and then sent to Oxford, openly to recant and carry a faggot, to the terror of the students of this University. On a Sunday he was brought into this church, many doctors, divines and citizens being present. Dr Smith preached the recantation sermon, and Mr Malary stood before him with his faggot. About the midst of the sermon, there was of a sudden heard in the church the voice of one crying 'Fire! Fire!' in the streets, occasioned by a person who saw a chimney on fire in All Saints parish, and so passing by the church cried 'Fire!', thinking no hurt. This sound of fire being heard in the church, went from one to another, till at length the doctors and preacher heard it themselves and began to look up to the top and walls of the church, which others seeing looked up also; upon which some began in the midst of the crowd to cry out 'Fire! Fire!' 'Where?' says one, and another. 'In the church,' says one. The word church was scarce pronounced, when in a moment there was a great cry, 'The church is on fire! The church is set on fire by heretics!'

This made them so afraid that they began to run away, but so great was the press of the multitude crowding together, that the more they laboured, the harder it was to get out, for they stuck so fast in the door there was no moving forward nor backward. They ran to another little wicket on the north side and from thence to a door on the west, but there was so great a throng that with the force thereof a great bar of iron was pulled out and broken by the strength of men's hands, and yet the door could not be opened for the vast concourse of people.

At length, despairing of getting out, they ran up and down, crying out that 'the heretics had conspired their death'; one said he plainly heard the fire, another affirmed he saw it, and a third swore he felt the melted lead dropping on his head and shoulders. None made more noise than the doctor that preached, who cried out in the pulpit, 'These are the subtleties of the heretics against me. Lord have mercy upon me.' In all this consternation, nothing was more feared than the melting of the lead, which many affirmed they felt dropping on their bodies. The doctors finding authority and force could not prevail, fell to entreaties, one offering twenty pounds, another his scarlet gown, if any man would pull him out, though it were by the ears.

A boy had climbed up on the top of the church door, and seeing a monk coming towards him, with a wide cowl hanging at his back, he thought it a good opportunity to make his escape, and jumped into the monk's cowl. The monk got out with the boy in his cowl, but feeling his cowl heavier than ordinary, and hearing a voice behind him, he was more afraid than while in the throng, believing that the evil spirit which had fired the church had flown into his cowl, whereupon he began to exorcise: 'In the name of God and all saints, I command thee to declare what thou art behind my back.' 'I am Bertram's boy,' said the other. 'But I,' said the monk, 'adjure thee, in the name of the inseparable Trinity, that thou, wicked spirit, do tell me who thou art, and from whence thou comest, and that thou go hence.' 'I am Bertram's boy,' said he, 'and I pray, let me go.' When the monk perceived the matter, he took the boy out, who ran away as fast as he could.

The story is all too plausible, right up to the bit about Bertram's boy, but there the credulity begins to waver. 'Feeling his cowl heavier than ordinary'? With a boy in it he would hardly have been able to move. It all goes to prove that you should always go back to original documents if you want the unvarnished truth. As later chapters will show, however, sometimes sworn testimony of several witnesses paints a picture which stretches one's capacity for belief to the utmost. . . .

CHAPTER FIVE

COVINGTON: THE ARCH VILLAIN?

Most localities have a favourite villain – someone who manages to worm his way into the popular consciousness by some means or other, and stands subtly aside from the throng of evildoers. Whitechapel has Jack the Ripper; Oxfordshire has Giles Freeman Covington. One difference between them is that everyone knows what the Ripper did, but his identity remains uncertain, whereas there is no question of Covington's identity, but a lot of uncertainty about precisely what he did. The other major difference is that the Ripper was spectacular if unpleasant, whereas Covington was pitiful, but probably a nicer chap. Not that this made any difference to the pedlar David Chartres, who was never in a position to comment on the matter.

On Monday 8 October 1787 Chartres was at Abingdon Fair, plying his trade in a most profitable manner. Flushed with success and a fair amount of cash, he dropped in to a pub on the way home to Toot Baldon and may have made the mistake of flashing his money about. This was the last anyone saw of him. His body was discovered in a ditch near Lord Harcourt's Park three days later. Christopher Willoughby, the local justice of the peace, offered a reward of 10 gns. for anyone bringing evidence which would convict the murderers; this was not a spectacular temptation, as he was offering the same amount to trace the person who had stolen his laundry. Lord Harcourt stepped in and the reward rose to 70 gns., which was a far greater temptation to turn in one's fellow man, irrespective of whether or not he was guilty.

The authorities examined the scene of the crime:

Was knocked down on the stile, as the stile was bloody and the ground was bloody where he lay. The ditch was about two yards from the stile.

At least five wounds on the head and supposed to have been given by a hedge stake. Skull not fractured. No money in his pocket, though he was known to have money in Abingdon and at the public house. His pockets seemed turned partly out.

They also had a list of possible suspects: 'Robert Latimer of Warborough, commonly called Jolly Robin. Benjamin Woolsgrove of Toot Baldon. Fisherman of Abingdon was seen to go with a sack by the public house. James Carter of Nuneham has often threatened him, and animosity between them.' Carter was in the traditional position of foremost suspect who is cleared by later evidence, as he and his wife were seen crossing the field by the stile shortly before Chartres set out from the pub, but Latimer was also in a position to have known about the money and followed the pedlar. Painstakingly witnesses were questioned to reconstruct the victim's last hours.

Parker overtook Chartres about a furlong from Rye Farm, about two or three acres' breadth before he came to a stile. They shook hands in the walk and asked each other how they did, and walked together to Water Turnpikes about 3 furlongs distant. It was about half past five when they first met. He was alone and likewise Parker. Parker went into the house first and Chartres followed. They did not sit down, but called for a pint of fresh beer. They found Latimer sitting down in the house by the window. They asked each other how they did, and Latimer asked him to drink with him, which he refused. Latimer then sung a verse of a song, and said Chartres sung it better than any man to please him, but he declined entering into any conversation, and seemed very shy of him. They only stayed about 7 or 8 minutes. There were several people in the house. Parker came out of the house first and Chartres followed immediately. They walked together, then they parted and wished each other a good night. Parker went up to Culham Common, and Chartres went across the Mead, and he saw him going through the meadow towards the wood, and after that time he saw him no more. He supposes he was home about a quarter past seven. It was quite light when he left Chartres to go along the Mead. Is very positive he left Latimer in Turnpike House.

Latimer certainly wasn't going to admit to being in a position to sneak out after Chartres and use a hedge stake on him. He claimed that he was in the company of Benjamin Paty and his wife all the way from Abingdon to Dorchester, and that anyway he left Chartres in the Water Turnpikes rather than following him out. This clash of evidence could have been very embarrassing to one or other party, had not John King and James Patey made it irrelevant. The two of them were returning from the fair to Dorchester, when they observed four men at a place called Ditch End, just on from Water Turnpike, three of whom King recognized as John Castle, Richard Kilby and Charles Evans Shury. Chartres could be seen proceeding across the meadow ahead of them, but as this was a perfectly normal state of affairs King and Patey proceeded on their way until they were crossing Culham Heath, when they were stopped in their tracks by a terrible cry which seemed to come from the spot where the body was later found. Unheroically they decided to continue on their way, but 70 gns. was enough to tempt them into court.

The three men they named would certainly have come under suspicion sooner or later. They were well-known local villains, involved in various petty crimes which were brought out to blacken their characters in the subsequent proceedings. A number of linen thefts were laid to their account, together with the matter of James Bridgeman's pigeons and Mr Wyatt's fowls. In the shadow of the gallows, the local rogue Thomas Smith was prevailed upon to recount the story of the Revd Mr Nichols' horse, which did Shury's reputation no good:

Parson Nichols of Sutton, Berks, had by some means given offence to Charles Shury of Abingdon, and Shury out of revenge wished the Parson's horse to be stolen, and accordingly sent to Smith for that purpose, telling him that he could help him to such a thing. Shury took Smith there under a pretence of showing him how a dog would behave in the field, that Shury had to sell; but the true intent was to examine the horse, whether it was worth taking away or not. The horse was not then in the churchyard; however, Shury the same evening sent a man, a companion of his by name Kilby, to see if the horse was there. If it was Kilby was to bring it back with him. He found it and rode it out of Abingdon one mile, when he delivered it into Smith's possession, for which Smith gave two guineas to Shury and one to Kilby. Shury wished Smith to return to Abingdon as soon as he could, for he could help him to a famous horse of Mr Phillips of Culham, worth 100 guineas, and that likewise he had a key to every door in Mr Phillips' house, as well as stables and outbuildings. He likewise informed him of a sporting gentleman in the neighbourhood of Abingdon, whose sister is disordered in her mind, and whose servant is very intimately acquainted with Shury, and for a bribe of five guineas would convey his master's horse to Shury to be given into the possession of Smith. *Mr Shury, please to remember when you stole Lord North's gold and silver pheasants out of Bushey Park.*

The magistrates of the day were much inclined to believe that a man who stole horses would do worse; still, it was a giant step from that to murder. Unfortunately there was a strong suspicion that this step had been taken before Chartres came on the scene; a woman had been found murdered at Culham Bridge, and a bargeman called Whitehead claimed to have heard Castle boasting of it. Castle was certainly the weak link in the gang, as he seemed to have a positively psychopathic compulsion to confess all his evildoing to passing bargemen. When the three men were arrested, an astonishing number of bargemen, or people who knew bargemen, came out of the woodwork to hammer nails in their coffins:

Peter Peckman of Abingdon, brewer, on his oath sayeth that as he was writing a letter at the Half Moon near the Great Church between six and seven o'clock in the morning, Joseph Crawford of Abingdon, bargeman, came into the public house where there were several people drinking, and entered into conversation with them, and said that he had heard Castle say as they were sitting down in the hatches on board the barge, that he was one of the persons that swung the woman over Culham Bridge, and that he had hold either of the hands or legs, and that he helped throw her over the bridge, and that either Kilby or Covington was with him and threw her over, and that he knew who did the Scotchman [Chartres], that he was present, and that after they said he was dead, a woman who was likewise present said 'Damn his blood, draw him among the stinging nettles', and that there was a great deal more conversation, the particulars of which he cannot recollect, as he was busy in writing his letter.

John Brown of Abingdon, bargeman, on his oath sayeth that he has heard John Castle say that if he was taken and admitted in evidence, that he would discover who the persons were that committed the murder at Culham Bridge and the man at Nuneham. . . .

William Barden of Abingdon, bargeman, on his oath sayeth that he has heard John Castle say to the effect mentioned in John Brown's deposition, and that he would take a great many of them down that carried their heads very high in Abingdon, and he has often declared that in case he was taken that he was certain of being hanged. . . .

Pausing only to wonder what the general run of conversation was like in the Half Moon, Abingdon, if the landlord found his letter writing more interesting than a murder confession, it is worth noting that here for the first time the fourth man is named: Covington. The problem was that even with his name and description, he couldn't be found. The other three were picked up, although Castle, of all people, tried to brazen it out with an alibi. A letter exists from Henry Deane, one of the Reading magistrates, to his colleagues in Oxford:

> Castle was brought to me quite cool this morning, but he still persists in his innocence. Colonel Powney and Mr Hodgkinson (our chaplain) were both present, and both declare they never saw a more hardened man. He depends on proving an alibi. He was acting, he says, as waiter at some public house the whole of the day and evening on which the murder was committed. . . .

Meanwhile Kilby and Shury met in gaol, and Shury suggested that Kilby tell the authorities all he knew. This attitude rather surprised Kilby, who replied, 'Then I shall injure you, Charles – but I suppose you want me to confess that you may do me.' Shury had other ideas in mind: 'No, boy, for you shall be evidence along with me.' This was an aspect of the case which may already have occurred to Kilby. If the two of them turned King's evidence and pinned the crime on Castle and Covington, they had a fair chance of walking out of court free men. The more he thought about it, the more attractive the proposition seemed. Then he thought about it some more, and saw a possible snag: one man might get away with it, but the court was unlikely to stand for two men sliding out of its clutches. He turned Shury down. Shury realized why a fraction too late.

The trial took place in July 1790. Various witnesses to aspects of the case came forward, then the prosecution produced its trump card: Richard Kilby, who was prepared to tell all, on the understanding that he was only a relatively innocent bystander. To Shury's horror he heard Kilby tell a version of the story which put him squarely in the centre of events:

> In the afternoon of the day on which the murder was committed, Shury applied to him and the other two accomplices, informing them that he would help them to a good booty in robbing an old Scotchman on his way home. That they afterwards met at Shury's house, where they agreed to the proposal, and about five o'clock in the evening Shury and Castle went first, and in about ten minutes were followed by him and Covington. That they joined company near the Water Turnpike, but about Ditch End again separated, Kilby keeping the path whilst Shury, Covington and Castle kept to the left towards

the river. That they all four again joined company, and as soon as Chartres had got over the stile, Shury struck him a violent blow on the head with a hedge stake, which blow was instantly followed by others from him and Covington till they judged him dead, himself and Castle being all this while a few yards distant, till Covington called for assistance to roll the body into the ditch. That Castle and Kilby returned together to Abingdon to Shury's house, and met with him and Covington, where the booty was divided, Shury giving each of them in gold and silver ten guineas, saying 'Now, my boys, let us be true to each other'.

In the light of subsequent events the last words appear singularly ironic; but then the whole account is slightly suspect. Perhaps it really did happen that way. Yet it was an odd coincidence that the two men who actually committed the murder turn out to be Shury, whom Kilby was expecting to turn King's evidence himself and so had to be got out of the way, and Covington, who wasn't there to defend himself. And there is no mention of the sinister woman with her 'Damn his blood', despite the fact that Castle had mentioned her when he had nothing to gain from it, and it seems a very eccentric detail to make up. Shury's defending counsel tried to discredit Kilby, but failed:

It was attempted to show that on meeting the Abingdon coachman at the gateway of the Bell in Holborn, Kilby had used expressions tending to manifest a design of what is called 'doing' Shury, but it appeared that he was only enquiring if any handbills were brought to London relative to the stolen pigeons.

It is difficult to imagine any form of words which could be construed in such vastly differing ways, but perhaps the authorities were none too keen on having their star witness discredited. He had, after all, cost them a lot of money. His price for stabbing his friends in the back was a free pardon, the bill for which survives: £88 10s. 6d. – free, in this context, meant free to Kilby. Shury and Castle both went to the gallows. That should have sewn it all up, but there was one disquieting loose end. The mysterious Mr Covington was still at large.

Kilby had dropped the fourth man well and truly in it, and the hunt was on. A description was circulated:

Giles Covington, aged about 20 years, born at Abingdon, has lived there ever since, five feet nine inches high, very stout and well made, flaxen hair, pale complexion, light grey eyes, long visage, large, long nose, remarkably gruff in speech, mostly wears a blue coat with plain white metal buttons, white linen waistcoat, brown corduroy breeches, walks very upright, rather swaggering in his gait, supposed to be on board an Indiaman.

This last was the secret of his success; he was a sailor, and hence could run further than anyone else. During the period since the murder he had married, on 5 February 1789 in Abingdon, which suggests that the heat was not yet on. His son was born on 7 May 1790, and christened at St Sepulchre's, Holborn, so he may already have been on the run. Sampson Wright, an officer of the law, was after him, and when the trail came to a full stop on the dockside soon found a way of tracking his quarry:

The assurances of assistance which I received from the Admiralty satisfy me that the getting of this delinquent into custody will not be attended with any difficulty, though it certainly cannot be done without expense.

He was picked up as soon as his ship came into a British port, and placed in the custody of the Bow Street runners. Returned to stand trial, he soon found Kilby ready and willing to step into the witness box and testify against him:

Kilby on his oath sayeth that the person now produced before him is Giles Covington, and that the said Giles Covington was one of the persons that robbed and murdered David Chartres, a travelling Scotchman, about three years ago at Nuneham, and that the said Giles Covington struck David Chartres after he was knocked down by Charles Evans Shury and that this deponent, Shury and John Castle were all present when the said Chartres was murdered.

Shury had remained silent when Kilby betrayed him; Covington was less phlegmatic. As Kilby spoke, he broke from the dock and aimed a blow at the witness' head, but failed to make it connect. After a brief trial the jury brought in an immediate verdict of guilty, and Covington was led away. Kilby's evidence was scarcely required. When Covington was arrested on leaving his ship, *Jackson's Oxford Journal* had referred to him quite openly as 'this most atrocious offender', and it seems likely that the idea of his guilt had been firmly instilled into the jury before they even saw the man. What happened next is the reason why the shadowy Covington, rather than Shury or Castle, is the man always remembered in the case.

COVINGTON: THE ARCH VILLAIN?

Covington refused to admit that he was guilty, even after it made no difference. In the condemned cell, the night before his execution, he wrote a letter, semi-literate but comprehensible, to Christopher Willoughby, the magistrate in the case, in which he made this perfectly clear:

> Sir — I have trouble you with these few lines concern this horrid affair which I am in Oxon Castle for or at least which is laid to my charge. There is no doubt, Sir, you been at a deal of trouble about it and a deal of expense, but, Sir Willoughby, how happy tis for me to go to this untimely end, which I expect in a short time, and to call God to be a witness and he to deny it for me, which I can with a safe conscience, I thank God for it.
>
> There is no doubt but the poor man lost his life, but, Sir Willoughby, it not found out it, and so you will find when tis too late for me. But it not only, Sir, taking my life. There is the poor widow that will be left to go in the wide world, and my poor mother and father with sorrow to their graves, but the hope to make theirself happy, more so than if I had been guilty of it, which I am not, I thank God. I hope that you and your family will live to find that Giles Freeman Covington is innocent, and then I hope you will relieve the widow that left behind if bedlam is not her doom, instead of putting my life, being gone, which will be of no further service. So no more at present from the unfortunate youth, Giles Freeman Covington. I hope God will be with you and yours.

The letter was completely unnecessary. It was too late for a reprieve; indeed, Covington does not ask for one, evidently resigned to his fate. There seems no reason for a protestation of innocence other than the obvious one: that he was, in fact, innocent. But if so, what are we to make of a letter to Willoughby from a certain Mr Lovegrove of Wallingford? It is undated, and is in all other respects a mysterious communication:

> Sir — There is a shopkeeper of respectable character named Joseph Deadman at Brightwell, Berks, near this place, who was some time since in Oxford Castle, and on observing to Giles Covington (with whom he had been once in company at Sutton) that *he was sorry to see him in that situation*, his answer was so remarkable, that out of love to public justice, I thought it necessary to send it to you. *I shall follow the rest of them and die with a lie in my mouth as they did.* Whether you shall or shall not see it necessary to subpoena Deadman to give evidence, you will be so obliging as not to mention that I have given you this information.

Does Covington mean that he will continue to protest his innocence to the end, even though it is untrue? Not one of the three ever admitted the murder. If so, why was he so stupid as to reveal his intentions to a respectable shopkeeper, who just happened to have dropped into the gaol for no readily apparent reason? For Lovegrove to think the information worth forwarding, it must have followed Covington's continued protestations of innocence after his condemnation, the last time he would be talking unguardedly to a man who must have had *agent provocateur* written all over him. In fact, the letter is so convenient from the authorities' point of view that it almost makes Covington's claim seem more rather than less plausible. Or does it just seem that way when read in conjunction with a letter from Daniel Harris, Keeper of the Gaol, to Willoughby, dated 7 March – the day of the execution?

Covington persisted in his innocence to the last with respect to the murder, though he has confessed that himself and Shury stole the church plate, that Kilby and him stole Tramplet's blankets, and that he perjured himself in the affair of the pigeons – which is the substance of everything he made known and which he declared was every affair of the kind he had been concerned in. He seemed quite resigned to his fate, his behaviour decent and becoming in every particular excepting his not acknowledging the murder. There could be no secrecy observed in what he did confess, for I hear tis generally spoken of up town. I would bring to your recollection that Shury protested equally violently his innocence of stealing the plate as of the murder, and several other little circumstances of that kind contradicting each other and themselves, which I think must remove every doubt (if any still suppose them innocent) from their minds. But I think some well directed paragraph should appear in the newspapers, to entirely clear up the business, notwithstanding it may not appear to be absolutely necessary. The circumstance of all three persisting in their innocence at the last moment causes some to have their doubts, I apprehend.

It must have seemed like a good idea to Willoughby. If the report of the execution in *Jackson's Oxford Journal* is not a masterpiece of biased reporting, it is a triumph of woolly thinking:

Having mounted the drop, he threw over a paper which he desired might be read aloud; it denied, as his confederates had also done, the fact for which he suffered. He had also confessed, among other things, the sacrilegiously robbing St Nicholas Church at Abingdon, in

Ser

I have Trobbulyou with thee few Lins
Consarn this horred afer with i ham in
oxon Gasel for oral Last With is Laid to
My Charge Ther is no douet Ser you
bin at a dal of Trobel a bot it &
a dael of exspenc bot Sir villabe hou
happey tis for me to go to this on timle
find Wich i exspaks in a short tim
and to tol god to be a Vitness & hee to
deniit for me Wich i Can Wich a Safte
Conshonsh i thank god for it
Ther is no douet the poor man Lost is Lifte
Bat Ser Villabe it not fond out it
and fou you old find Wend tis to Late for
me bot bot it onley Ser Taking my Life
Ther is the poor Viddew that Vill bee Left to
goe and the Vide Vorld and my Poor mother
and Feather Vith Sorow to ther Graves bot the
hoat to make ther selfe happey mor so
Then if I had bin Giltley of it with I han
Not I think god I ~~you and I hopto~~
I hope you and your Famley Vill Live to
find that Giles Freeman Covington did
hinhersent and Then I hop you old releve
the Viddew that Left bin if beedlum
~~dom~~ is not her dom insted of pulling my
Life bin gon Wich will be of no servis
So no mor ~~at present~~ from ~~you~~
the unfortnet youth Giles Freeman
Covington
I hope god Will bee With
you and yours

The final letter of Giles Freeman Covington, proclaiming his innocence to the last
(*Oxfordshire Archives*)

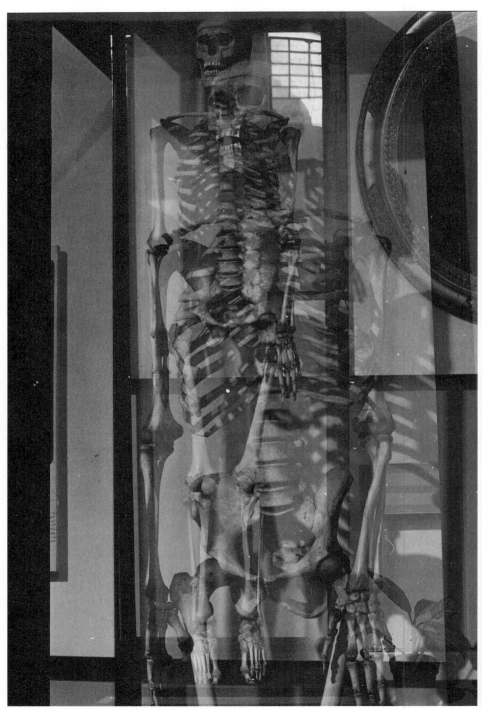

The last remains of Giles Freeman Covington (*Oxfordshire Archives*)

company with Shury, though Shury had positively denied this as he did the murder; and, in an unguarded moment, with some bitter imprecations, charged Kilby with falsehood and perjury in giving testimony that any of the blows were given by him to Chartres, well knowing that he was not at that time within the length of a couple of hop poles of his person. After conviction, he acknowledged divers crimes which at present it would be imprudent to divulge, but which would remove any doubt, could any remain, of his guilt. Hence we have only to lament the wickedness and depravity of human nature, that any hardened wretches should thus dare, in their dying moments, by attempting to impose upon credulous minds, insult an already offended deity.

And so Covington went to stand before a higher tribunal, and one which might have been less inclined to rely unquestioningly on the unsupported word of a man who was perfectly placed to have committed the crime himself. It did seem rather as if the precise identity of the murderer was of less interest to the court than sending at least three of the four men involved to the gallows. If they had to choose one of the four to go free, they could have done better than Kilby, who proved to be as greedy as the worst modern informer. Covington's final words from the scaffold were 'Beware of Kilby!' Daniel Harris later had cause to remember them:

> Kilby has wrote to me to say that he has got work at Cotton End near Northampton, that he at present lodges in a public house, and wishes me to send him some money, that may help him to buy goods to go into a private house. I would be guided what answer to send, but I can't help thinking his application somewhat too early. . . .

Meanwhile, Covington's body was delivered to the university anatomy school for dissection, in accordance with the Statute for Anatomizing, and he was forgotten. Many decades later, however, someone took a close look at the skeleton in the University Museum labelled simply 'Englishman', and saw, written on the left mandible, the words 'Giles Covington'. Out of all the criminals who had passed through the hands of the medical men, Covington had survived, at least in his bare bones. The skeleton has since been transferred to the Museum of Oxford, where the staff celebrated the two hundredth anniversary of his execution by petitioning the Home Office for a pardon. The Home Office politely turned down the request, but Covington lives on, longer in legend than he could ever have done by eking out his natural span.

CHAPTER SIX

CRIMINAL
PRACTICE

Most of the villains of Oxfordshire are loners, at least to the extent that their families don't keep turning up in the court records. There was only one Covington; some, like Mary Blandy, made sure that their families did not follow in their footsteps by poisoning them. These are the hard cases, the ones who go beyond a joke and end up in gaol or on the scaffold. But before plunging into the catalogue of crimes and corruption, pause a moment to consider one of the county's few recorded families of minor villains, the Coxeters of Bampton. Far more likely to be involved in a punch-up than anything more serious, they still chose the most inappropriate places to pick quarrels, usually the local church.

The number of pitched battles which broke out in church in past centuries often surprises us today. It shouldn't; individuals who hated, and so avoided, one another most of the time, had little choice but to come face to face for the Sunday services. On 11 January 1674 one of these brawls broke out in Bampton church. A certain John Nobbs, apparently irritated with the young girl sitting next to him, picked her up and threw her bodily out of the pew; he then kicked her prayer book out after her. Since the service was taking place at the time this caused something of a stir but not necessarily much surprise, since the girl in question was young Magdalen Coxeter.

In a close-knit community like Bampton, it can be difficult to track down the precise facts of a case. Ann Coxeter swore that she had seen Nobbs throw Magdalen out of her seat, and further that 'she saw Nobbs as he was kneeling on the bench with his back towards Magdalen, kick or thrust at her with his feet'; however, her name makes her testimony immediately suspect. Catherine Laine claimed that she saw him 'take Magdalen in his arms, in so much as she thought he would have thrown her over the seat, and therefore went out of her own seat to catch her'; but she turns out to be Magdalen's aunt, so not entirely unbiased. Thomas Ackers, who backs them up, is revealed as the cousin of John Coxeter, Magdalen's father. Fortunately, just as one begins to wonder if the entire congregation apart from John Nobbs is related to the girl, Thomas House appears. He saw exactly the same as the others, but he also saw something else: 'John Coxeter's daughter ran or thrust pins in John Nobbs' legs before he touched her'.

Why was the little demon sneaking into Nobbs' pew and sticking pins in his legs as he prayed? Well it might have had something to do with a long-standing quarrel between Nobbs and John Coxeter about which of them owned the pew. Following the Reformation a system of pew renting had developed, with the rich competing to possess the best pews in church, while the poor had to be content with a bench in the corner. Coxeter wanted the best pew, Nobbs had got his hands on it, so Coxeter sent the shock troops in and made it too uncomfortable to hold. It seems to have been not untypical.

Not that the Coxeters were negligible. They were of a status to become justices of the peace, although they had some difficulty staying in post. Forty years later, in the same church, they were at it again: 'Edward Johnson did say unto Richard Coxeter these words following: "I thought you would have denied your hand, it would be like you."' These stories without a beginning are infuriating; Johnson is obviously accusing Coxeter of having signed something which it would now be politic of him to know nothing about. Coxeter was stung by the allegation: 'What, do you think I am like you? A rogue, a rascal, a villain?'

This really annoyed Johnson: 'I am a better gentleman born than you, who are the grandson of a tailor, and are yourself a rogue and a villain, and are not now in the commission of the peace, having been turned out for bribery and forgery.' What Coxeter said to that nobody caught, but it must have been pretty scathing because Johnson invited him to step outside into the churchyard to continue the debate with his fists, and 'did use very much foul language to Richard Coxeter, and said that although there had been acts of indemnity passed, yet there were none for high treason or for clipping and coining, and that if Richard Coxeter had not fallen into the hands of gentlemen, he and his wife deserved to be hanged'.

Sure enough, investigation shows that Coxeter had been a justice, but had mysteriously left the bench, just at a time when the perennial Oxfordshire vice of forging currency was being investigated. It was a capital offence, but far from ending up on the gallows Coxeter wasn't even prosecuted. Perhaps there was no evidence; or perhaps Johnson was right, and Coxeter's connections had hushed the matter up. At any rate the family lived on to cause more trouble in the locality.

The Oxfordshire magistrates did tend to go easy on trivial crimes like treason. Shortly after the Glorious Revolution of 1688 those who continued to support the deposed King James II against William of Orange were riding for a fall, in most places. In Oxfordshire Thomas Kembar was going about conducting a recruiting campaign until Thomas Long informed on him:

> Thomas Long of Garsington says that Thomas Kembar of Littlemore met with him on the 18th day of March 1689, as he was going to Oxford, and told him that if he would go into Ireland and serve King James, he would help him to a horse of £20 price, and also help him to £20 more to carry with him, and likewise would give him a little to conduct him safely thither. And further sayeth that Thomas Kembar told him that many a man was undone and King James turned out of his kingdom by this King Pippin. And Thomas Kembar told him that he had provided four horses and men already to go.

Put like that the magistrates had no option but to intervene, although there is no indication of any draconian punishment being visited on the recruiting officer. Politics have always been a thorny subject, liable to raise strong passions in otherwise rational men. In the days before organized football matches, elections provided an excellent excuse for hooligans to run riot, and none was more than the closely fought 1754 Oxfordshire election. For the first time in decades the long standing Old Conservative group, known unsurprisingly as the Blues, was challenged by the New Interest Yellows, whose party line was a little uncertain, but which was basically another set of Conservatives who thought that the Old Conservatives were a little extreme in some of their stances – the hard-liners versus the wets, perhaps. There were several skirmishes between them as the campaign progressed, and on election day all hell broke loose.

'The election produced a spirit of party more violent and lasting than has been known for many years, and hurried both sides into excesses which must always be remembered with regret.' So *Jackson's Oxford Journal* put it, with generous understatement. As the returns were coming in the Yellows brought together a cavalcade of coaches and carriages, and started a progression from The Bear, then a famous coaching inn with a frontage to the High Street in Oxford, towards the east of the town. They were followed by a rabble of Blue supporters, 'who became every moment more numerous and more outrageous, pelting the chariots and coaches with dirt and stones, hurting many of the gentlemen and covering the carriages and the horses with filth'. On Magdalen Bridge, the mob surrounded a post-chaise with the obvious intention of doing lasting damage. Unfortunately for them, they chose the one containing Captain Turton. With cries of 'Over with them, drown them, damn them, kill them!' the crowd took hold of the carriage wheels and began to lift it off the ground. Inside, Turton calmly primed his pistol. A chimney sweeper in the crowd picked up two pebbles and threw them at the chaise. He was just bending down to pick up a third, when Turton leaned out of the window, levelled his pistol, and shot the man dead. While the crowd stared disbelievingly at the body, Turton and his post-chaise continued on their way. He was brought to trial for murder, and acquitted immediately on a plea of self-defence.

Not that the Yellows were without an undisciplined rabble of their own. Their mob broke into one of the Oxford churches, mounted the pulpit with a supply of alcohol, and drank 'Damnation to the last Blue parson that preached in this Blue pulpit'. Things reached such a pitch that innocent bystanders were dragged in. A visitor to the town had trouble with his horse's bridle, and his servant wound an old rag he had on him around it to keep it secure. Unfortunately the rag happened to be yellow. As the man rode into Oxford, he was, to his great surprise, mobbed by the Blue supporters, who took him for one of the enemy.

The trouble with mobs, even from the viewpoint of those who create them, is that they tend to be uncontrollable once they get under way. It takes a brave man to face them, or a brave woman. Ursula Jordan was married to a man who seems to have had little regard for the rights of others. The Jordan family turn up elsewhere in the records of Quarter Sessions, accused of enclosing common lands illegally for their own use. In May 1696 it seems likely that they had been engaged in this favourite activity on Eynsham Heath, although the fact is never stated. And on the evening of 23 May Ursula was informed that a large crowd of people had assembled to tear down a house that her husband had built on the heath, 'and to do other mischief to her husband's estate there'. In the late seventeenth century sending a message to the local police station was not an option, and most people would have found something urgent to do elsewhere; not Ursula, who saddled her horse and set out to discover what was going on. 'Being there, she saw several persons, some with guns, some with staves, some with pickaxes and other weapons, in a riotous and violent manner, to the number of two or three hundred, and she heard some of these persons in a menacing manner threaten to do mischief.'

Now this was a particularly good time to remember an important engagement elsewhere, since there was nothing an unarmed woman, or come to that Arnold Schwarzenegger, could do against those sort of odds. Yet Ursula stood her ground until William Stock, evidently one of the ringleaders, appeared. He took a party down to the nearby rabbit warrens with mattocks and spades; they dug out a number of rabbits, then chopped them in pieces and pelted her with them. The action is so macabre, so unnecessary, that one wonders if there was something symbolic to the case about the rabbits, or if Stock was just a very strange man. The opinion of the rabbits themselves is not recorded. However, it did bring home to Ursula Jordan the possibility that when they had run out of rabbits the mob might do something similar to her. When one of the participants approached her and held the club he was carrying against her head, she retreated to her house. The mob followed.

Faced with an angry crowd milling about outside the doors, she decided to reason with them, and 'desired them to withdraw and permit her to be in peace'. This seemed to be doing the trick, but she made a serious mistake in adding that she had sent for Justice Parrott to come down and command them to withdraw. Immediately they cried that they did not care a pin for him, and threatened that if the door were not opened to them they would break it down. When they actually started pulling the window frames out, Ursula decided to follow the road Captain Turton would later tread. She gathered the household around her, and when the mob started to break in she and the servants presented them with the business end of all the firearms in the house. This time it was not necessary to pull the triggers. The crowd melted off into the night, although not fast enough to prevent the ringleaders being recognized, and fined £40 for their share in the night's work.

It was by no means the first time that animals had been the catalyst in violence between humans, as any gamekeeper could testify. Take the sad tale of William and John Boice of Burford. Being 'very poor and necessitous', they took a trip to the Forest of Wychwood where they were allowed to help themselves to rabbits and vermin provided they left the game alone. Spotting several rabbits, they ran after them crying 'Kill them!' to one another, just as a party of gamekeepers rounded the bend. Regrettably the gamekeepers misinterpreted the situation, and defended themselves with rather more vigour than was strictly necessary; indeed they 'violently set upon William and John Boice, to their no small damage'. To add insult to injury, it was the battered Boices who ended up in court charged with poaching and intended assault.

Rather frequently in court records it does seem to be the poor who get the blame. Colin Dexter's novel *The Wench is Dead* is not a favourite work in Oxfordshire Archives, chiefly because of its implication that we don't know where to find the records of the Oxfordshire Assizes (of course, if a real-life Morse had come to ask us about them, he'd have been sent to the Public Record Office, found them all neatly catalogued and available, and there'd have been no plot); but Dexter does have a pretty accurate picture of the reputation enjoyed by the local canal boatmen in the nineteenth century. They did tend to be the sort of people who were presumed guilty until found innocent. However, it could be argued that the way some of them acted they had only themselves to blame.

On 2 July 1829 the inhabitants of Wolvercote were somewhat put out to find a group of young boatmen from Oxford running riot among their cows, ducks and geese on Port Meadow; two of the Wolvercote men, Robinson and Eeley, went over and requested them to stop. They seem to have known one another, as Robinson addressed one of the troublemakers by name: 'Tom, you ought to know better than to destroy poor men's property.' Thomas Beesley knew he was being accused of duck stealing, but decided to bluff it out with a sneer: 'Do you mean to say I have got one in my pocket?' The bluff was immediately called, not by Robinson but by the duck, which was indeed in Beesley's capacious pocket, and which chose that moment to start quacking. Obviously Beesley had to take the initiative quickly, but the way he chose to do it may say something about the canal boatmen. Most people would have run with the duck. Beesley and his friends attacked the Wolvercote men, chased them back into the centre of Wolvercote, and challenged the whole village to a fight.

This may have been a bad move, as they were now outnumbered. A couple of large, tough Wolvercote men decided to take them up on it and brought a bludgeon each along, just for good measure; the rest of the inhabitants gathered on the sidelines to watch the boatmen being beaten to a pulp. They were disappointed. Beesley rapidly disarmed one of the bludgeon carriers, and then created a diversion by questionable tactics: he attacked the crowd. To be exact, he went for a man named John Barrett, who was an easy victim as he wasn't even watching the fight; he was talking to someone and had his back turned. Beesley struck him a tremendous blow on the back of the head, and the unfortunate bystander died the following day in the infirmary.

Beesley was arrested, but his friends weren't going to desert him as easily as that. They attacked the constabulary and set him free. This did him no good in the long run as he was simply arrested again, but it was useful for the purposes of later historians, as the authorities were forced to issue a description of the man they wished to interview, and it survives as a rare physical description of one of that legendary group of water-going desperadoes:

About 30 years of age, about 5 feet 7 inches in height, middle sized, light complexion, rather freckled face, rather dark hair, whiskers a little sandy, had on a pair of fustian trousers, red plush waistcoat with brown fustian sleeves, and a pair of half boots, a black leather cap bound round with fur; walks rather stiffly with one leg.

Incidentally, the affair proved that the courts weren't always against the boatmen on principle. Beesley was convicted of manslaughter, which, considering he had started the affair by duckstealing, had pursued his opponents, had issued the challenge to fight, and had killed an innocent man by hitting him from behind, was remarkably lenient. Perhaps the boatmen were simply lucky; they'd found someone even poorer than themselves to take the blame.

It would be naïve to assume that crimes of violence were the prerogative of the poorer classes. The rich could be just as violent, with an element of cunning mixed in which makes the whole business more chilling. Among the rich, the stakes were generally worth playing for. A duck is a fairly pitiful prize to be worth anyone's life; in the mid-eighteenth century, £12,000 was enough to tempt even a man's nearest and dearest.

Francis Blandy, eminent Attorney-at-Law, was the well-respected Town Clerk of Henley-on-Thames. His wife died in 1749, leaving him with an only child, his daughter Mary, who had just turned thirty and was spoken of even by those who had no reason to wish her well as 'of a middle size, well-shaped, of a brown complexion, with black eyes full of fire; and though not a beauty is very agreeable, especially when she speaks, and her conversation is full of wit and good sense'. Like most men of his era, Blandy must have been concerned about his daughter's chances in the marriage market; though not unattractive she was no spring chicken by the standards of the age, and this evidently led him to give out some not-entirely-accurate information on the state of his fortune and the possibilities of her dowry. It was an exaggeration he was to regret.

One man who was ensnared by it was a certain Captain Cranston, a Scottish officer, who became a frequent visitor at the house. There seems to have been no attempt to deny him access, but Blandy made it clear to his daughter that she should not form any attachment to the man, as he was suspected of having a wife still living in Scotland. This made absolutely no difference; Mary Blandy had become obsessed with Cranston, and rapidly grew to see her father as the one obstacle to their marriage. Cranston, on the other hand, had become obsessed with Blandy's fortune, and saw the old man as the one obstacle to his getting hold of it. It was a bleak outlook for Francis Blandy from all angles.

Thus it was that one morning in early August 1751 a package arrived for Miss Blandy from Scotland, containing some Scots pebbles to make her a pair of earrings, and a powder to clean them. The pebbles were merely a pretext to get the powder into the house unsuspected; no more is ever heard of them, but the powder rapidly took centre stage. On 5 August Mary made her father his water-gruel, and quietly mixed some of the powder in with it. Blandy senior happily ate the mixture and went about his business. He didn't quite finish the bowl, but left it on the table. At this point his daughter began to get some lessons in the difficulty of a good, clean poisoning job when there are other people about the house. The charwoman, a poor washerwoman called Mrs Hemmet, spotted the leftovers and, being hungry, ate them. They carried her home in a chair, groaning and vomiting; 'she continued dangerously ill for a long time, that her life was despaired of, but she is now able to walk abroad, though it is thought she will never recover so as to be quite well again'. In one or two minds, the first suspicions began to form that something odd was going on.

The following day, an identical concoction was sent up to Francis Blandy, and this time the leftovers were sent back to the kitchen. Mary was passing through the kitchen at the time, and she stuck a spoon in the gruel and brought it out full of a white sediment. She quickly passed it off with the observation that the oatmeal looked very white, and stirred it back in again, but the two maidservants had seen it and remembered the last thing Mrs Hemmet had eaten before being carried out. They decided to keep their eyes open, but unfortunately for one of them, they were looking in the wrong direction.

Mary realized that there was no quicker way of attracting suspicion than by sticking to one method of administering the poison, until everyone spotted the distressing effects of eating water-gruel in the Blandy household. She tried the powder in tea, but it wouldn't dissolve properly and she emptied the cup out of the window. Susannah Gunnell, the chambermaid, noticed the cup and decided to make herself a nice, refreshing cup of tea; being a slovenly creature, she didn't bother to rinse the cup out first, and received a rather brutal lesson in the virtues of good housekeeping. 'Though she is now recovered,' observed a contemporary commentator, 'she is wore down to a skeleton.'

It seemed that Mary was going to wipe out the entire household before she finally got to her father, but the steady diet did have its effect on him. His health was visibly deteriorating, and he complained of pains in his bowels. The servants were increasingly convinced that he was being poisoned, and went with their suspicions to Mrs Mountney, an acquaintance of the family. She sent for the local apothecary, Mr Norton, who tested the white powder which was coming down from the dining-room every day, yet could not work out what it was. 'But let it be what it will,' he said, 'sure that stuff has no business there.' Nor was there any doubt about who was behind it. Apart from the circumstantial evidence, Mary had been talking much too freely with the cook, calling her father a toothless old rogue (which was a touch callous, since it was her arsenic powder which was making his teeth fall out), and telling her that he would be dead before October. When asked how she could be so sure, she replied that Captain Cranston had visited a conjuror in Scotland, who had told him that some of the family would die before that time.

This left them with the problem of explaining to their master that his own daughter was trying to kill him. Fortunately their task was made easier by the old man having his own suspicions. 'Poor, lovesick girl,' he is reported as saying. 'What will not a woman do for the man she loves?' On 9 August he made his way down to the kitchen, where his daughter was at the time, and asked the cook what time of the month it was. 'Well,' he said, 'about this time of the year Queen Anne was poisoned. I remember that a long while ago, being in company at the Red Lion, they gave us some damned stuff to drink which poisoned us all. One died, and I was very sick with it.' Then he turned and looked sternly at Mary. 'I am afraid that it will be my lot to be poisoned.' His daughter was clearly stunned by the obvious implication, but forced a smile and answered, 'Papa, it is twenty years ago since that happened. I remember it very well.' She then hurriedly left the room. When she had gone he poured his tea into the cat's bowl, which alienates a good deal of sympathy from him.

From that time on, Blandy kept to his room, and refused to let his daughter in to see him. She begged to be allowed in, but he remained firm until it was evident that he could not last much longer. Then, finally, he called her in, and spoke to her as she sat on the foot of the bed. 'My dear girl,' he said, 'I forgive thee with all my heart, but will hang Cranston if I can. Be gone.' He never spoke to her again, and died on the 14th.

Mary knew she was in serious trouble. Far from her father dying of unknown causes, leaving her to play the distraught daughter, stories of his poisoning were flying about the town. On Sunday 11 August she was actually accused of the crime by Mr Littleton, her father's clerk, at the instigation of the servants. After his final words to her, Blandy had confined her to her room with two men watching her, and anything she might have used to commit suicide taken away. No sooner had her father died than a letter arrived from Cranston, which was intercepted by the doctors; it was couched in the sort of innocent terms by which the immensely stupid expect to escape suspicion, and included the line: 'Above all, don't spare the

The Coxeters' favourite fighting ground – Bampton church (*Centre for Oxfordshire Studies*)

Feelings ran high in the 1754 Oxfordshire election, as this contemporary cartoon shows (*Oxfordshire*

The furthest Mary Blandy managed to run – Henley Bridge and the Angel alehouse (*Centre for Oxfordshire Studies*)

Mary Blandy takes tea with a friend shortly before her execution (*Oxfordshire Archives*)

powder, in order to keep the pebbles clean.' There was no chance now of remaining in Henley as the respected, bereaved daughter; her best chance was to destroy all the evidence she could and run.

First, she brought down all Cranston's letters and piled them on the kitchen fire; into the flames with them went a small paper of powder, which the servants noticed burned bluish. After she had left with the words 'Now I am pretty easy', they raked the paper out, and found written on it 'Powder for cleaning Scotch pebbles'. The two men set to watch her were dismissed; with her father's death she was mistress of the household and could give the orders. Tradition dictated that one of the servants should sit up with her for the night after her father's death, but she refused to consider it, saying, 'The night is my own, and I will have whom I please.' In fact she had already approached her servant, Robert Harman, with an offer of £500 to get her away, but he had refused and told Mr Littleton. Littleton was in a quandary. First he gathered together two of his friends and another gentleman from the town and stationed them at the front door of the Blandy residence to see if she did make an escape, but he knew his legal position was risky, and he then went to a local lawyer for advice. The lawyer bluntly told him that there was no warrant out for Mary Blandy, so none of them had any right to be in her house except with her express consent, and Harman could accept the £500 without fear. Littleton then went to see the Mayor and Corporation of Henley, who were meeting in the Catherine Wheel, and they agreed to send a constable to watch her. The constable duly arrived, and refused to have anything to do with the affair, saying that as Miss Blandy had not been consigned to his custody, he had no business there.

So far the law was on Mary Blandy's side. Unless she was formally accused of poisoning her father, she had the right to go where she liked and do what she wanted. On the other hand, she was having some difficulty in finding anyone who would help her to do so. She asked the cook to get her a post-chaise and accompany her to the west of England; the cook refused. With no one to accompany her, she dared not leave the house that night, but the next morning dressed, took cash and notes to the value of £1,000, and set out on foot. She got as far as Henley churchyard before some children recognized her, and they drew a crowd of people who followed her to the bridge, thinking that she was going to throw herself in the river. In fact she had no intention of doing anything of the sort, nor did she intend to give the mob the chance to turn nasty. Instead she took refuge in the Angel alehouse, on the Berkshire side of the river, and when the Corporation of Henley sent its officers to stop her going any further, they found her calmly consuming a pint of wine and a toast.

Now, for the first time, the authorities began to indicate that she was regarded as a suspected murderess. Politely but firmly they brought her back to her house in a post-chaise, claiming that it was to save her from possible violence by the mob, and kept her there while the inquest on her father took place. The coroner had no doubt that the man had been poisoned, and his daughter was held for questioning. There was no way she could claim not to have been feeding mysterious powders to her father; the servants would testify to that, even if they hadn't seen anything. Instead, she fell back on the clumsy defence that she hadn't realized that the powders were poisonous, having been told by Captain Cranston that they were a form of love potion, and would increase her father's affection for her. Perhaps they did; not many parents would forgive their offspring for poisoning them in a particularly painful manner because they had been refused permission to commit bigamy. It is only fair to say that the authorities did not believe her, and sent her to Oxford gaol.

This was in the days before modern egalitarianism; a convicted murderer would end up just as dead at the end of exactly the same rope whether he were prince or pauper, but his journey there would be very different according to his social status. Mary Blandy was allowed to delay her arrival at the gaol in order that she might have time to pack all the clothes she needed; she brought with her a serving woman, Mrs Dean, and her favourite tea chest, full of the finest hyson. She was, of course, going among friends. Her father, as Town Clerk of Henley, had been a close friend of magistrates and officials, and the daughter was in the ambiguous position of knowing the men who were putting her on trial for her life. It was one of these friends who brought her the final irony: the assessment of Francis Blandy's estate. The man who had claimed to be worth £12,000 was found to have less than £4,000. If Cranston had known that, he would have been less inclined to pursue her; without Cranston she would never have committed the murder. On hearing that there was a warrant out for her lover's arrest, she commented, 'I pray God they may take the villain, that he may suffer, for it is all owing to his request and advice.' But Cranston was well away before the warrant reached him.

Mary Blandy was found guilty, and sentenced to the gallows. Her final request was that she might not be hanged too high for decency's sake, bearing in mind the crowds who always flocked round the foot of the scaffold, eager for a cheap thrill.

It was to be many years before the Kalabergo case started people wondering if public executions were really that good an idea. William Kalabergo was an Italian immigrant in Banbury. He was also one of the most staggeringly incompetent murderers in Oxfordshire; another of those villains who liked to keep it in the family, his victim was his uncle,

Kalabergo the clockmaker, whose timepieces are still in demand to this day.

John Kalabergo had emigrated to England from Lombardy to escape conscription under Napoleon. During the following decades he built up a thriving business, but kept in contact with his family in Italy, and in 1851 agreed to his nephew William joining him for a time in Banbury. William had a dubious reputation in his home village, and his uncle was hoping that he could reform the boy into someone fit to take over the business. He had a naïve way of going about it, starting as he meant to continue. Bringing a youth who had been allowed to run wild with no discipline all his life into a foreign country, he then proceeded to impose a set of rules on him which would not have been out of place in a monastery. Kalabergo insisted that he should be respected and obeyed, and that his nephew should never answer back, that there should be no drinking or gambling or smoking, that William was curfewed after nightfall, and that he should attend confession and take communion regularly. An average young man would have found some of these restraints irksome; to someone who had caroused around the neighbourhood night after night for the best part of his life, they must have seemed intolerable.

William Kalabergo in his turn started as he meant to go on, by arriving in England on a forged passport. He wasn't in the best of moods anyway, as he had fallen rather heavily for a personable young lady named Maria back in Italy, and uncle had told him to lay off in no uncertain terms. The strict regime in the Kalabergo household did not help, and before long William was pondering on the information he had received from elsewhere in the family that he was one of the major beneficiaries of uncle's will. He set about meeting the conditions for inheritance.

His first move, on 15 December, was to provide himself with a weapon. He took himself off to a gunsmith on Butcher Row, and bought a revolver. This was his first mistake; by Oxfordshire standards Banbury was a large town, but not so large that a swarthy individual with a thick Italian accent and a barely comprehensible grasp of English wasn't going to be remembered. Thinking this over later, William realized the possibility that he might be identified, so he took the weapon along to Holland's, another gunsmith in the town, and changed it. This now made two local gunsmiths who could recognize him at a distance of fifty paces. Evidently deciding that he had now made himself sufficiently conspicuous, he set to work making bullets for the gun. In the 1850s, it was necessary to buy a bullet mould, metal, percussion caps and so forth to engage in a do-it-yourself operation. Having created enough ammunition, he hid the equipment in the place most likely to be searched after the murder, the loft of the stable behind Kalabergo's shop. All he needed now was an opportunity.

This came sooner than he could have hoped. Kalabergo senior was in the habit of making regular trips around the district with a cart of merchandise. Shortly after Christmas he took his nephew with him on one of these. His nephew took the gun. Still his ineptitude as a would-be murderer dogged him; on the journey the two men ran into a number of uncle's friends, who would unquestionably be able to identify his travelling companion, but William persisted in his purpose. Finally, he got his uncle alone. As they struggled up Williamscote Hill, Kalabergo junior slid the gun out of his pocket and shot his uncle in the back of the head.

He had been seen travelling with uncle, he had hidden the bullet mould in the most obvious place, and two reputable tradesmen could swear to his buying the gun. Yet William Kalabergo felt there was still a possibility he would get away with it. He promptly took action to make this possibility even more remote. First, he ran away leaving his hat on the road beside uncle's body. Second, realizing he was heading back towards Banbury holding the murder weapon, he threw it away into a ditch, but was careful to wrap his coat around it first so that it could be traced back to him. Then he started to make up his story.

In itself the story wasn't a bad one, because it was so simple and, in those lawless times, quite plausible. William claimed that three men had attacked and tried to rob them on the road. When John resisted they had killed him and he, William, had run for his life. This accounted for the hat by the body and the proof that he had been travelling with uncle, but for precious little else. He went immediately to tell John's friend, the Catholic priest Dr Tandy, who roused the authorities to go and search for the body. They found it with no trouble. They also found an untouched wallet in the victim's pocket, and a cart standing by the roadside loaded with valuable merchandise. No one had told William that when footpads attack and rob people, they generally take their loot away with them. The story of the robbery immediately started to look very flimsy.

It wasn't long before the story of the gun came out. William claimed that John had asked him to buy it and given him the money to do so; in fact, he had stolen the money from John's shop. The explanation tied up very badly with the gunpowder and exploded percussion cap found in William's pocket. The authorities started to search the Kalabergo premises, and in a very short time reached the stables. William was arrested on a charge of murder.

One thing Kalabergo junior could not have known was that forensic investigation was making rapid strides forward in the mid-nineteenth century. The idea that the bullet in uncle's brain could, and would, be matched to the mould in the stables would never have crossed his mind.

William was transferred in a purposeful manner from Banbury to Wroxham gaol, and decided to make a break for it. In this he was as incompetent as in everything else, and the only thing he succeeded in breaking was his leg. So obvious did his guilt seem, that when the Home Office was asked for an interpreter to cope with Kalabergo's obscure Italian dialect at the trial, the reply came back that a foreigner committing murder in this country must find his own interpreter, which seemed to be prejudging the issue a little. The authorities were still not entirely happy; for a watertight case, they needed the gun.

They knew the boy must have thrown it away in his flight, but in the middle of winter the area was flooded and it could have been lying anywhere. Mills were ordered to let down their sluices and gates to clear the area, and the ploy worked. The gun, and Kalabergo's coat, were found and identified. William Kalabergo was hanged for the murder of his uncle. That, however, was where the real story began.

Dr Tandy, the priest, spent a good deal of time with Kalabergo before his execution. The boy had murdered one of Tandy's oldest friends, but the priest could see that stupidity and clumsiness rather than malice were at the heart of the crime. He also saw the terror of the boy as the scaffold approached, and was one of the witnesses to the execution. It seemed to him that a public hanging was more sickening than the crime itself. Afterwards he had a few well-chosen words with the prison governor on the ugliness of the spectacle; the governor was inclined to agree, and passed the message on. From that point, the opposition to such undignified proceedings grew. Kalabergo is now remembered as the last man to be publicly executed in Oxfordshire, so perhaps some good came out of his crime in the end.

The stresses and strains on those who administer justice have always been considerable in one way or another. Small wonder that some of them show signs of irregularity from time to time. In 1837, down the road at the Berkshire Quarter Sessions, the clerk of the peace showed less signs of irregularity than every indication of having gone off his head. As the court was proceeding with its administrative business at the Midsummer Sessions, William Budd – the said clerk – entered the courtroom, leapt on to the table, and sat down on the large box containing the Statutes at Large, ordering the court crier to call for the Bailiffs of the Hundreds. When he had recovered sufficiently to believe his eyes, the chairman of the bench told the crier to do nothing of the sort, but Budd insisted, claiming that he and not the chairman was the representative of the court. The crier decided it was wiser to side with the chairman, so Budd turned to his own assistant, Mr Vincent, and ordered him to do it; Vincent dodged the issue by claiming that he hadn't got their names with him. By this time the chairman was beginning to shake himself free of the disbelieving horror which had gripped him, and told Budd that 'his conduct was very disrespectful to the Bench'; Budd replied, illustrating his speech with a number of graphic gestures, that he knew the chairman would like to put him under the table if he could, and that a good many people would like to bury him before his time, but he had retained counsel if they wanted to try him.

By this time the magistrates were scandalized, and one of them, Mr Mount, insisted that the court must take note of such behaviour. Budd turned on him: 'Who are you? Nothing but a Parliamentary stationer, that is have been, mind I say, have been.' Another magistrate, the Revd Mr Dodson, exclaimed that it was too bad, and promptly drew Budd's fire: 'I suppose you're a second Vicar of Bray, who like all your cloth would change sides.' By this time it should have been obvious that Budd had it in for the entire court, and that the best thing to do was for the magistrates to keep their mouths shut while someone manhandled the clerk out of the room, but the bench didn't seem to realize this. Mr Eyston piped up next, and was told by Budd in a most offensive manner that he knew who he was, a Roman Catholic who knew the advantage of a majority of numbers. When no one else volunteered to be a target for Budd's sarcasm, the clerk let fly at the whole court, saying that they thought they were all captains, and he was just the poor cook among them.

It was later decided that Budd must have been drunk, and that he was a most unfit person for the position of clerk of the peace. Yet one wonders. The nineteenth-century bench was not always noted for the intelligence and humility of its magistrates, and there is a limit to the length of time a rational man can suffer under a cabal of pompous bureaucrats. Perhaps he had simply had enough. One shudders to think what he might have said had he encountered Sir John Croke on the bench.

Croke was the baronet of Chilton House, and as such had employed Robert Hawkins, perpetual curate of Chilton, as his private chaplain since 1665. Hawkins' salary was £50 a year, which was extraordinarily generous, but this was no skin off Sir John Croke's nose as he never paid it. Eventually Hawkins was forced to start legal action against Croke for his money, and it is at this point that our story begins. For the curate was very surprised, shortly after commencing court proceedings, to find himself in the dock on a charge of felony, and before none other than the magistrate Sir John Croke himself.

Henry Larimore, an inhabitant of Chilton, swore that on Friday 18 September 1668, just after noon, he and his family left their house, locking the doors after them, and went off to work their land, some two furlongs away. They worked until evening, but on returning home found, to their horror, that the doors were open. Larimore ran inside, up to a room above the chamber in which he usually slept, when he suddenly heard a noise from below; bending down to look through a crack in the floorboards, he saw none other than Robert Hawkins ransacking the box in which he kept his valuables, removing a white holland apron, a purse containing two gold rings, two pieces of gold and several shillings. These Hawkins pocketed, then ran out of the house, waving a large bunch of skeleton keys to show how he'd got in in the first place.

Larimore, deciding that this was the sort of pastoral visit he could do without, went to the magistrate Sir Richard Piggot of Doddershall and obtained a search warrant; then the following day he took the local constable and hammered on Hawkins' door, demanding admittance. Hawkins decided he would be safer keeping the door locked, so they broke it down and searched the house. In an inner room, Larimore found one of the gold rings which had been stolen, together with a 5s. piece he strongly suspected of being his property. He told the constable to arrest Hawkins, and brought him to the Assizes, before Croke.

It was obviously an open and shut case. Larimore's son confirmed all that his father had said. Richard Mayne, the constable, did say that when Larimore brought the warrant to him, he said nothing about actually having seen Hawkins commit the crime, and that they had searched other houses, but the stolen items had certainly been found in Hawkins' house, and indeed Hawkins was present in the room when they were discovered. Margaret, Larimore's wife, swore that she had seen Hawkins lurking around the house of another Chilton inhabitant at night, evidently for nefarious purposes, while Dodsworth Croke, Sir John's own son, gave evidence that he had pawned the stolen ring to Larimore himself, and that he recognized it as Larimore's property. That, it seemed, was the end of Hawkins' promising career as a man of the cloth, until, that is, the prosecution made the mistake of calling one more witness, a man by the appropriate name of Chilton, the local shoemaker.

Chilton was called to swear that Hawkins had stolen a pair of boots out of his shop, as proof of the man's generally dishonest nature. To the great interest of the court, Chilton, when asked if it was true that Hawkins had stolen the boots, replied that no, it was not. Before anyone could shut him up, he went on to say that he had received a visit from Larimore and Dodsworth Croke, who had tried to force him to give evidence against Hawkins, offering him £500 if he did so and several months in a prison cell if he did not. Faced with that sort of pressure the only way he could protect himself was by bringing the whole affair into a court of law, so he had evidently pretended to go along with them until he had the chance to make a public statement. The court grew thoughtful as the case for the defence began.

The first attack was launched on Mayne, the constable. Witnesses showed that far from Hawkins being in the room when the gold ring was found, he had been deliberately held in the hall by two of Mayne's friends, so that Larimore was alone in the room when he claimed to have discovered his property, or what he claimed to be his property; other witnesses said that Larimore certainly used to have a gold ring, but that he had lost it nine months earlier. On top of this, closer investigation of the arrest and bringing to trial of Hawkins showed that Mayne had gone to considerable lengths to have the curate tried before Sir John Croke, despite the fact that the quarrel between them was common knowledge.

The circumstances were so odd that someone thought to have a look at the original search warrant, whereupon they grew even odder, as the warrant proved to be dated the day before the robbery was supposed to have taken place. After which it came as no surprise when Mr Charles Wilcox, a man of good repute, swore that he was visiting Larimore on 18 September, that he was there all the afternoon, and that not only was Hawkins conspicuous by his absence, but Larimore himself never left the house all day. Why, the court mused, should Larimore go to such lengths to frame Hawkins? The answer came in a petition from more than a hundred inhabitants of Chilton, claiming that Larimore was an Anabaptist, an enemy of the Church of England, a hater of the clergy, and particularly ill disposed towards Hawkins, who had indicted him for non-attendance at church. The case for the prosecution was falling to pieces, and Sir John Croke must have resigned himself to the fact that he wasn't going to win his battle over Hawkins' stipend by default, when suddenly the last witness appeared and opened a yawning pit at the magistrate's feet.

Mr Browne, an officer of the Court of King's Bench, had been staying at Croke's house in the week before the alleged robbery; to be precise, he was keeping an eye on Croke due to certain other suspicions held against him. Hearing a noise in the night, and suspecting that Croke might have decided to absent himself from the district for a while, he crept downstairs to check, but found that all was well. He was just about to return to bed when he heard voices in the dining-room, and thought it might be wise to listen in. Croke's visitor was Larimore, and the two men were discussing Hawkins. In fact Croke was instructing Larimore to get a warrant from Piggot, take Mayne, and search Hawkins' house, 'and there,' he said, 'you will find these things. Then charge him with felony, force him before me and no other

Justice, and I will send him to gaol without bail and hang him at the next Assizes'.

It was at this point that Sir John Croke was observed to rise and leave the court. His fellow justice on the bench then broke legal precedent by giving evidence himself, to wit that Croke had that very morning sent him a present of sugar loaves with a letter suggesting the verdict he would like in the Hawkins case. The summing up refreshingly concentrated on the shortcomings of the judge rather than those of the prisoner, and Hawkins left the court without a stain on his character. Which is more than can be said for Sir John Croke.

Croke got his just desserts, but by due process of law. Few people are able to call a curse down when they consider the court is rigged against them, and get their revenge by visiting plagues on their persecutors. In fact the only person in Oxfordshire who ever managed it was Rowland Jencks; at least popular belief credited him with doing so, and one has to admit that there were some odd coincidences going round the Shire Hall of Oxfordshire back in 1577.

Jencks was referred to as a saucy bookseller, which doesn't mean that he sold saucy books, but that he was a saucy man who sold books. In fact his books said much the same sort of thing that he did, namely that the Church of England was a heresy, the state was as bad, and Queen Elizabeth I was not at all a nice person. Not many people said this openly in the later sixteenth century, or if they did they didn't say it for long, and Jencks had a good run for his money, largely because he was bookseller to the university and thus, in a sense, a privileged person. However, there came a time when the university decided that he wasn't the sort of person they wished to be protecting, and they sent him to London to be examined by the Queen's Council. Details of the examination were sent back to Oxford, Jencks' house was searched for seditious and irreligious writings, and the man himself was committed for trial at the Assizes on 4 July.

The trial lasted two days, and the outcome was a foregone conclusion: Jencks was sentenced to lose his ears. Legend credits him with having cursed the court before he was taken away, but this sounds very like a later addition to the story; Jencks was a devout Catholic, and unlikely to be making deals with the devil. Nevertheless, no sooner had he been removed from the court than a dreadful stench started to spread through the building, choking those present and infecting them with some virulent disease which killed them in a matter of hours. All those on the bench died, together with most of the jury, and a good proportion of the bystanders in the courtroom. But the plague didn't stop there. It got out of the Shire Hall and started to cut a swathe through the city. According to an eyewitness, over six hundred people fell ill with it in one night, three hundred of whom died. The wind carried it into the neighbouring villages where it caught another two hundred.

> The whole number that died in that time were 510 persons, of whom many bled till they expired. The time without doubt was very calamitous and full of sorrow; some leaving their beds, occasioned by the rage of their disease and pain, would beat their keepers or nurses, and drive them from their presence. Others like madmen would run about the streets, markets, lanes and other places. Some again would leap headlong into deep waters. The physicians fled, not to avoid trouble, which more and more came upon them, but to save themselves and theirs.

Then it vanished as suddenly as it had come. Certain things about its course added to the legend of what became known as the Black Assize: the fact that no women were affected by it, no visitors to the town, and strangest of all none of the poor. It really did seem to have been aimed at those who had condemned the bookseller. Now we know the infection to have been gaol fever, caused by the cramped, insanitary condition of the prisoners in the cells beneath the courtroom; not that this gets us much further, as no one is quite sure just what gaol fever was. But one man proved that it was possible to stand right in the middle of the infection and survive. Rowland Jencks walked from the court, emigrated to Douai, became baker to the College of English Seculars there, and died an old man in 1610. Odd, that.

The old Shire Hall was abandoned by the court for nearly three hundred years in almost superstitious fear. Only in the nineteenth century did the area gradually come back into use, by which time it was impossible to say exactly where the event had taken place. Insofar as it can be pinned down, the site of the Black Assize is today occupied by the County Record Office. We try not to think about it.

Gaols have often been insanitary places. Only one prison cell in Oxfordshire has ever qualified for an ecology award, and that was Judge Morton's favourite lock-up on Kidlington Green. Because of the difficulties of transporting prisoners to Oxford gaol late at night, he used a gigantic hollow tree, not unlike the one which sheltered the poor woman in Bletchingdon, to hold them until the following morning. The tree was said to be 25 feet in circumference, which gives it a diameter of about 5 feet 8 inches − enough for the average seventeenth-century malefactor to stretch out. One of the strangest prisons in the county was the perfectly conventional one in Thame. Its strangeness stemmed from the way that someone attempted to privatize it rather early in its history.

By his will of 21 July 1643 Richard Baker of Thame left seven small tenements to the use of the poor, the churchwardens of the town having the responsibility of deciding which poor should be put in them. This was all very generous of him, so much so that the churchwardens failed to notice a small clause in the will which was going to cause problems fifty years later. In 1693 there was a sizeable fire in Thame which destroyed six of the tenements, and the sorrow of the parishioners at losing these houses for the poor was as nothing to their sorrow when they realized that they were legally obliged to rebuild them at their own expense.

It was at this point that one Francis Clerke Esquire made a suggestion which would at least maximize the benefit to be got out of rebuilding. He pointed out that so rapidly were the poor of the parish increasing that seven tenements were no longer a great deal of use; instead, they should build a workhouse in which large numbers of the poor could be made to earn their keep. The derelict site of the six houses was large enough to add a house of correction, in which the evildoers of the locality could be taught the error of their ways. Clerke died before the work was completed, but still contrived to put more into the project than everyone else by leaving the income from his estate – some £50 a year – to finish the building, and then to provide stock to set the poor to work in the workhouse and the criminals to work in the house of correction. Anyone who has ever asked if it is a crime to be poor might care to ponder the way in which the two groups were treated almost identically.

Having created the building, the parish needed someone to run it; they appointed Robert Perry, a West Countryman, to be in charge of the house of correction. However, Perry had rather an odd notion of the sort of behaviour expected from a prison governor: 'he had two persons committed to him from Quarter Sessions to be kept at hard labour for twelve months, both of which he let out to work, one at eight shillings [40p] a week, the other at six shillings [30p] a week, took their money, and let them escape'. Having thus increased his salary, he got to work on his accommodation. The house of correction was built to hold two keepers and their families as well as the inmates and the poor, but Perry claimed that it wasn't nearly big enough, and evicted the last poor person from the one tenement which had not burned down. He then married his son off to a local girl and gave them the house as a wedding present. Just to round things off, he then threw the poor out of the building in order to give himself more elbow room, and settled down to administer the house of correction from there.

This upset the parishioners of Thame, who had intended to put their hard-earned money into building a workhouse, not extensive accommodation for the local gaoler. They complained to Quarter Sessions on a delightful point of poetic justice. Perry's family, they said, was enormous and not inclined to hard work. If he married them all off to inhabitants of Thame, the parish would be responsible for them when they were reduced to paupers. Alas, it would not be able to help them, because Perry had effectively destroyed the workhouse and taken over the one remaining tenement. The only way to help Perry's family would be to throw him out of his place and reconstitute the workhouse. It was necessary to be cruel to be kind. The magistrates agreed, and Perry found himself looking for another job.

The Thame parishioners now found themselves in the difficult position of having a gaol without a gaoler; however, this was a minor inconvenience to set against being able to claw back Perry's palatial residence and reconstitute the workhouse accommodation. It cost them £100 for the rebuilding work, but this didn't worry them as Clerke had left the income of his estate to cover that sort of thing. There was £250 waiting for them in the hands of the Master in Chancery, and when the work was completed they went to collect it. To their dismay, they discovered that the money had vanished. Investigation revealed that it had apparently been drawn out by Clerke himself, which was a little disturbing as they had watched him being buried a couple of years previously. If one dismisses the idea that their benefactor was a member of the undead, the inference seems to be that someone had played a very efficient confidence trick. They never saw the money again.

Obviously they were going to have to dig into their own pockets to replace Perry; they did so and found William Twynam, whom they described as 'a very honest person to manage and look after their poor', thereby proving once again what astonishingly bad judges of character they were. Next to Twynam, Perry was an amateur. A few years later they were back petitioning Quarter Sessions, claiming that 'William Twynam, the keeper, lives at Aylesbury, six miles from Thame, and has for three years last past solely resided there, and the house of correction has been managed by his deputies, sometimes by girls only, and now by Giles Wiggins'.

Wiggins was worse than Perry and Twynam put together. On taking over the house of correction, his first discovery was that people kept locking all the outside doors of the building. This made it very inconvenient for him to fetch water from the well in the yard, so to stop them doing it in future he took the main door off its hinges. This in turn made it rather difficult to keep the prisoners inside, but that was no problem, as 'prisoners are

TRIAL AND LAMENTATION OF
KALABERGO,
FOR THE
MURDER
OF HIS UNCLE, AT BANBURY.

Intense interest and anxiety were excited in this town and neighbourhood by this approaching trial, and the doors of the court were beseiged long before the hour appointed for its commencement. At eight o'clock the proceedings began.

Mr. Keating, Q. C. and Mr. Cripps, for the prosecution; Mr. Pigott and Mr. Huddlestone, for the defence.

Mr. Maggioni, professor of Italian of the Royal Academy of Music in London, was sworn as interpreter of the evidence to the prisoner.

His Lordship directed Mr. Maggioni to interpret the questions and answers to the prisoner as they occurred.

The prisoner pleaded not guilty.

On being asked if he would be tried by a jury of Englishmen, or a jury composed of half Englishmen and half aliens, he said he should leave it to the Court to do what they thought best for him. His council decided to have a jury of Englishmen. The Court was densely crowded, and it was with the greatest difficulty that the door-keepers could preserve anything like order. When the prisoner came into the dock he presented a much better appearance than when in the court on Monday. His long bushy hair had been trimmed, and his

Louisa Egg, examined by Mr. Cripps—I lived with my sister at John Kalabergo's. I remember the Saturday evening the prisoner came home. I was called by Sophia Roberts. The prisoner was in the sitting-room. I asked what was the matter. He said "Uncle's dead" several times; he made motions with his hands of a person striking; he said "Three men" several times; he was much agitated; I stayed with him till Dr. Tandy came. The prisoner did not go out. Never saw the prisoner with a pistol, bullet-mould, caps, or gun-powder. (Two hats were produced, which the witness said were Mr. Kalabergo's and the prisoner's.)

Cross-examined by Mr. Pigott—I was not used to be in Mr. Kalabergo's room. The prisoner seemed to be in great distress and cried very much.

Sarah Hodgkins, examined by Mr. Keating—Stated that the prisoner and his uncle were at the Falcon Inn, at Prior's Marston, the day preceding the murder—they slept and breakfasted, and then went out. They had dinner, and left in the cart about half past 3 or a quarter to 4. They took the road to Banbury. When they went out in the morning. Mr. Kalabergo asked for a stick. He had one which he brought back and left. He had on a dark great coat when he came; I don't know if he had one on when he left; there were two or three coats.

George Hammond, examined by Mr. Cripps—Saw the prisoner and his uncle together at the Falcon, on the Saturday afternoon, at 2 o'clock; saw them after

had met without a driver. I took hold of the sleeve and found a man's hand. It turned out to be the body of John Kalabergo. He was lying on his face, with his face down hill. Ward and Ryrie went into Williamscote for a cart, I remained with the body. Trentham came up with the trap-cart, and I took possession of it.

Bernhard Samuelson, examined by Mr. Keating—I am an ironfounder at Banbury; I speak Italian a little. On the evening of the 10th of January, I went to the house of John Kalabergo. I had not known him. I saw the prisoner there. I went 3 times; first between seven and eight. I asked him what was the matter. He appeared very much distressed and agitated, so that he was coming down a hill with his uncle, they were attacked on the road and asked his uncle for his life or his purse. His uncle raised a stick he had in his hand and aimed a blow at him. Another man fired a shot at his uncle, and there was another shot fired; and that he was pursued by a third man across the fields. The man called out "Stop stop," and pursued him for eight or ten minutes. I went a second time about ten o'clock. I again saw the prisoner. I asked if he had lost his hat; he said he had. He did not recollect where he lost it. I asked if he ran up the hill or down. He said he left the road twice. He also said he met a man with a horse and cart, and endeavoured to alarm him, but the man could not understand him. He described the clothes of the men; two had dark clothes on, and the third light

Transcript of the Kalabergo murder trial, published as a broadsheet for the enjoyment of the locals (*Oxfordshire Archives*)

Old Banbury around the time of the Kalabergo murder (*Centre for Oxfordshire Studies*)

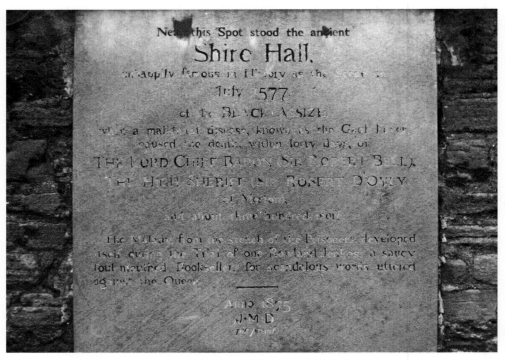

Tablet recording the site of the 1577 Black Assize, just above the cataloguing room of the present County Record Office (*Oxfordshire Archives*)

The petition of Sarah Pearpoint, forerunner of today's car crime specialists (*Oxfordshire Archives*)

permitted to go at large, and not kept to hard labour, and Mary Almond, committed for having a bastard, now goeth where she thinks fit'. Wiggins now had an empty prison, which a lesser man might have thought was no use to anyone, but the keeper was an entrepreneur to match any modern city wide boy. Faced with an empty building in a prime site, he did the obvious: he rented it out. 'He doth let part of the Bridewell to lay corn in, and the other part to lodgers.' He knew how to speculate to accumulate. 'He hath taken down the cubby holes for the lodging of prisoners, and used the boards to make a stable.'

Fortunately Wiggins isn't around to tender for any aspects of the prison service today. The magistrates took a dim view of his methods and sacked him, bringing the Thame house of correction saga to an end. Many prisoners in Oxfordshire would have been grateful to have a gaoler like Giles Wiggins. It could be a hard life in a seventeenth- or eighteenth-century prison, and a number of gaolers were corrupt in quite a different way from the speculator of Thame. Once inside prisoners had to fend for themselves, and those without friends on the outside could find themselves in dire straits. In October 1692 Sarah Pearpoint was found guilty of stealing the linings out of coaches – roughly the seventeenth-century equivalent of ripping out car stereos – and sentenced to a term in Oxford gaol. Four months later she sent a petition to the magistrates:

Your poor, distressed petitioner hath been detained close prisoner in the castle of Oxford ever since the beginning of October last, having neither friends nor means whereby to subsist, and having nothing allowed her whereby to live upon, so that I was forced to sell my clothes off my back. I hope your worships will consider my condition. And I in duty shall ever pray for your health and happiness in this world, and eternal felicity in that which is to come.

How heartfelt her prayers were when the petition was filed with 'Nothing' scrawled across it can be left to the imagination. Eventually the magistrates relented and allowed her a pittance, but it was scarcely enough to keep her alive. One can only hope that she received it. At the same time a petition was sent to the same magistrates from another four poor prisoners, who seemed to have a shrewder idea of how the system worked:

Your petitioners have undergone a tedious confinement, having no assistance from any friends, nor allowance from the county, but what comes from the hands of some gentlemen of the University, which is about a groat a week in bread. Your petitioners are in a most miserable condition, lying in the dungeon, and for want of relief your petitioners are forced to apply themselves to your worships, or else your petitioners must inevitably starve. Wherefore your petitioners humbly implore your worships to take their sad wants into consideration, that your petitioners may have some allowance from the county, what your worships shall think fit, and *ordered into those hands to be given to your poor petitioners as they may not be defrauded.*

Gaolers were not, by and large, well paid, and the temptation to divert the money sent to relieve the prisoners to their own use was enormous. In 1701 there is a note of one prison keeper relieving the poorer inmates out of his own pocket, although he is shortly found asking the magistrates for an increase in salary, being unable to make ends meet. Others of his calling were sometimes difficult to distinguish from the villains they guarded. In 1832, the case of Henry Doswell of Oxford gaol came to the notice of the magistrates:

The visiting magistrates are obliged to notice the bad conduct of Henry Doswell, the head turnkey. Some money had been given to him by one of the prisoners for the purpose of providing professional assistance for his defence on his trial at the Sessions: £3. The governor having been informed of this, he spoke to Doswell on Wednesday 26 September and desired he would place it in his hands. On the next day, not having received it, he applied to him again. Very soon after, Doswell left the gaol, giving no notice of his intention, and did not return till the following Tuesday, 2 October. During his absence, it was ascertained that he had received various sums from different prisoners to the amount of £8 or more, some from prisoners who were still in gaol, and some from those who had left the prison. The visiting magistrates have thought it proper to suspend him from the execution of his duties. . . .

He was duly dismissed. But he was part of a long tradition of prison officials who descended to rather undignified behaviour to achieve their ends. Solomon Wisdom, keeper of the gaol in 1786, was one such, although his objective wasn't money. It was revenge.

One morning in that year a thick sheet of paper was found nailed to the gate of the prison. On it was sketched what can only be described as a satirical cartoon. A figure was seen standing on a heap of something undistinguishable, and from the figure's mouth came the words 'I am cock of this dunghill, damme'. A hideous devil's head intruded into one side of the picture, saying 'Well done, my child Dan.', and the whole was labelled 'Daniel Damnable'. To the casual observer it must have seemed completely incomprehensible, but to those familiar with Oxford Castle and gaol it would spark off one immediate connection: the clerk of works at the castle rejoiced in the name of Daniel Harris. When the magistrates saw it, it brought to mind a certain problem they had been having recently.

Within the debtors' yard of the prison, a pile of earth and rubbish had been heaped up. Solomon Wisdom strongly objected to its presence in his nice, clean prison, but the magistrates insisted he was not to touch it. Accustomed to being obeyed without question, they were extremely surprised when Wisdom organized a party of debtors to move the heap further back into the yard, where it promptly blocked the drains. They repeated their instructions in a firm, clear manner, but Wisdom took no notice whatsoever, simply continuing to remove the earth and prevent the water gathering around the foundations of the building from escaping. Showing remarkable forbearance, the magistrates did not transfer him to the other side of one of the locked doors in the gaol; they told Harris, the clerk of works, to deal with him. Precisely how Harris did this is unknown, but the earth stopped moving abruptly. Shortly afterwards the cartoon appeared.

This looked like an open and shut case, but the evidence was only circumstantial, and when the drawing was shown to Wisdom he claimed that he had never seen it before in his life. The magistrates visited the prison, to find a set of debtors whose wide-eyed innocence equalled that of Wisdom, which wasn't surprising, because if anyone had squealed on the keeper the quality of his already miserable existence would have deteriorated in short order. The following day, however, they received a letter:

> I have taken the liberty to address you upon the subject I so impertinently detained you upon yesterday. If this confession can be any contrition to intenuate my offence in relating those palpable falsehoods I so rudely filled your worships' ears with yesterday, I here offer it to you with the most profound respect. Your reverence is sensible how ill I have been treated by Mr Wisdom, and if you'll but recollect about two years ago, when you and the Reverend Dr Onslow could not take my information respecting an assault made upon me by the keeper my case was then overbalanced by the false accusations and aspersions exhibited against me by the keeper, and fear of ill treatment made me yesterday deviate from the truth. Mr Wisdom applied to me and desired me to draw or sketch out Mr Harris and exhibit him in some ridiculous situation. I imprudently obeyed him, and then showed

it to many of the debtors and Mr Wisdom, who seemed to enjoy it as an innocent joke.

I then left it in the gateway. Who stuck it up, or by what means it came upon the gate, I cannot take it upon myself to demonstrate. A debtor was in the gateway, whose name is John Townsend, and heard Mr Wisdom make the request, as also was one if not both the turnkeys. If I am not happy enough to experience your worships' interference, I shall now lead the life of the most unfortunate of my fellows. I expect nothing now but impertinent and oppressive treatment. – David Gadsdon

The magistrates went to Wisdom and asked if he really knew nothing about the cartoon. When he denied all knowledge, they showed him Gadsdon's letter. He claimed it was a conspiracy; he might even have got away with it, had it not been for the small matter of the rubbish heap and the blocked drains. The magistrates were looking for an opportunity to get rid of Wisdom, and they grasped it with both hands.

Justice triumphed; Wisdom got his just desserts, Gadsdon was freed from his persecution, Harris was avenged for the caricature, and the magistrates disposed of the man who, they said, 'has been repugnant to every plan of reform lately introduced by the magistrates in the gaol'. Yet every silver lining has a cloud; Daniel Harris had acted so well in the affair that the magistrates promoted him to fill Wisdom's place as keeper. Five years later (if you cast your mind back a chapter) Harris was the man who sent Covington to the gallows and set up a smear piece against him in *Jackson's Oxford Journal*.

With this sort of thing going on in the prison, it is hardly surprising that many inmates made strenuous attempts to get out. In the medieval period this was not difficult; the place was so ruinous that prisoners tended to walk out through the holes in the walls. By the nineteenth century things were a lot tougher; still, the old trick of faking your way into the prison infirmary and escaping over the roof worked more than once, and one group of prisoners managed to knock part of the wall down even that late. For sheer ingenuity, the prize must go to Robert Harris and his brilliant escape plot of 1833. The prize would be larger if he had actually managed to escape.

Harris (no relation of Daniel) realized that the best plots are the simplest, and his plan was simplicity itself. He was in gaol for assaulting the constable of Chipping Norton and was still awaiting trial. Under such circumstances he would be allowed to go free if he could find two men to go surety for him, and he could get clean away if the sureties didn't mind losing large sums of bail. Harris' genius was in realizing that the two sureties were

Oxford castle and gaol, so ruuinous that prisoners escaped through the holes in the walls (*Oxfordshire Archives*)

'Daniel Damnable', the cartoon which mysteriously appeared on the gate of Oxford gaol in 1786 (*Oxfordshire Archives*)

Chastleton
May 11 th 1833

Sir

I do hereby authorise you
to Discharge Robt Harris from your
County Gool Oxford as James Mace
and John anker are become sureties and
bound in a bond of forty Pounds each
for his appearance at the next
General Quater Sessions oxford
before me J W Jones one of his
Majesty Justices of the Peace for the
Said County of oxford   I am yours respectfully

J W Jones

Received this Letter

Robert Harris' singularly unconvincing imitation of a justice of the peace (*Oxfordshire Archives*) completely unnecessary as long as people could be persuaded that they existed, and that the best way to do that would be for a magistrate to swear that they did. So really all that was needed to get him out was a single letter from a magistrate to Grant, the prison governor, and that was a comparatively easy job of forgery.

Harris could write, but not well. He therefore approached a fellow prisoner, Thomas Phillips, who was known for writing a very good hand, and tried repeatedly to persuade him to write the letter for him, but Phillips patiently explained to him the draconian penalty for forgery and his own reluctance to undergo it for the sake of Harris' personal freedom. Harris set to work to practise himself, drafting several attempts and destroying them, until finally he achieved something he thought was good enough. Then he sidled back to Phillips, and said, 'How should you direct a letter to Mr Grant, Phillips? You know better than I do, suppose you direct it for me?' Phillips was either terminally stupid, or didn't believe that writing an address constituted forgery, because he replied, 'Oh, I should direct it' so and so. 'If you wish, I'll direct it for you,' and proceeded to do so. The prosecution was later to make great play of the fact that Phillips was not known for stupidity, as they gently roped him in as an accessory to the fact.

Harris wasn't entirely stupid either, at least not so much so that he couldn't see how a letter purporting to come from a Chipping Norton magistrate and posted inside the gaol would fail to convince. He enclosed the letter in another one addressed to his brother-in-law, James Turner of Church Street, Chipping Norton, and sent it out via a carpenter who was putting up a fence in the gaol. The following day, Turner received a puzzling missive which contained a sealed letter addressed to the governor of the gaol in which his wife's brother was locked up, together with the following note:

Do not open the other letter, but put in the post as soon as you get it. Be sure it will do me a good deal of good. I am your affectionate brother-in-law, Robert Harris. Let nothing stop you from posting the letter.

Turner was later described by the prosecution as 'a very honest person', although doubtless Harris could have found other phrases to describe him. His immediate reaction was to say, 'That letter shall never be put into the post by me,' and indeed it never was. However, his wife persuaded him not to follow his first instincts and burn it, and later she sneaked it out of the house and into the hands of a small girl who was passing, giving her a farthing to post it. It arrived on the governor's desk the next morning, and its instructions were quite explicit:

Sir — I do hereby authorise you to discharge Robert Harris from your County Goal Oxford as James Mace and John ankers are become sureties and bound in a bond of forty pounds each for his appearance at the next General Quater Sessions Oxford befor me J W Jones one of his Majesty Justices of the Peace for the said County of Oxford.

That 'Goal' was a bad mistake; so was the small 'a' on 'ankers', the missing 'r' in 'Quater', the rather idiosyncratic spelling of 'befor', and the apparent inability to make 'Majesty' into a possessive. Grant started investigating the provenance of the letter. A messenger to Chipping Norton soon found an entire family willing to turn King's Evidence against their black sheep, and another brilliant plan bit the dust. Fortunately for Harris, Phillips was wrong about one thing. Faking the letter constituted a misdemeanour, not forgery, and added no more than a few months to the culprit's sentence. Judging by the usual run of incompetent sinners and villains in Oxfordshire, he almost comes out as a success story.

CHAPTER SEVEN

LOOKING VERY UNHEALTHY

If you were one of the unfortunate victims of the Oxfordshire sinners and villains, and managed to be wounded or injured in some way, it might have saved you a lot of trouble simply to die before you reached hospital. Once they got you inside your chances were slim indeed. This, of course, reflected the generally low standard or understanding of medicine before the twentieth century; it also reflected one or two very odd individuals who found their way into the medical profession.

The Radcliffe Infirmary, now a place to which I for one have reason to be grateful, was a far less prepossessing institution in the eighteenth century. In December 1777 the *Oxford Journal* reported the death of one Martha Jewell, who had been in the infirmary for five weeks with dropsy – sad, but in no way unusual. What was unusual was the discovery made when the staff cleared out her belongings from the box under the bed. In it was the body of a baby girl, which had apparently been born eleven days previously. No one even knew that the woman had been pregnant, much less given birth. The beds were four posters with curtains, affording a high level of privacy; nevertheless, there had to be something suspect about a nursing staff who failed to notice what was going on. Moreover, there had to be something odd about the atmosphere in the ward, when a body which had been decomposing for eleven days couldn't be smelt.

To do them justice, the medical staff did try to keep up to date with all the latest developments in treatment. Some patients might have wished that they would stick to traditional methods. In 1822, the Revd L.C. Lee of New College gave £400 to the Royal Sea-Bathing Infirmary at Margate, in return for the reservation of four beds for the Radcliffe Infirmary. Patients were sent regularly to Margate, where they bathed daily, were wrapped in sea-soaked sheets, found themselves sprayed with sea water, and were forced to drink the stuff both hot and cold. Back in Oxford at the same time the infirmary was building a special fever block, and to cheer the patients up, improving texts were placed on the walls in the various wards. The one in the fever block ran, 'Oh Lord, thou hast indeed brought me very low'.

The problem was that when a medical innovation appeared which actually did some good, it could be guaranteed that someone would oppose it. In the 1860s, in Glasgow, Joseph Lister developed his antiseptic system to combat the putrefaction of wounds. He experimented with carbolic acid, and in a few years had eliminated septic diseases from his wards, including tetanus and hospital gangrene. By the 1870s his methods were being brought into the Radcliffe Infirmary. A hospital which had previously been insanitary with poor ventilation, smells from wounds, straw mattresses in which the straw was not replaced regularly, poorly washed sheets changed only once a month and dirty blankets was taken in hand by the house surgeon Dr Palmer, and Listerian practices introduced. Unfortunately Palmer had reckoned without Dr Hussey. Edward Hussey had been at the infirmary for twenty years; he didn't believe in these new-fangled methods, and when he couldn't stop Palmer he complained to the hospital board: 'The House seems to be at the mercy of a young house surgeon, who is doing his best to poison the patients with carbolic acid.'

Hussey was rapidly becoming a menace. He was on duty at the time of the great Shipton railway disaster in 1874, when forty-seven of the injured were brought into the Radcliffe. The doctor attempted to put them in a ward with a group of diphtheria victims, telling those who tried to prevent him that this modern theory about the existence of germs was a lot of nonsense. Fortunately he was restrained. Events reached a climax in 1877, when Hussey managed to have himself appointed coroner to the city. Shortly afterwards a woman was brought in badly wounded after a fight with her husband. Hussey operated, failed to find the source of the haemorrhage, and his patient died. This might have been embarrassing for any other surgeon, but not for the city coroner. He held an inquest, found that his own conduct was above reproach, and closed the case. The hospital committee was less than happy. It resolved that 'Mr Hussey makes his choice which of the two offices of Surgeon to the Hospital or Coroner to the City he would hold'. Fortunately for the well-being of his patients Hussey chose the office of coroner, where at least he couldn't actually kill anyone; in this post he enquired with immense diligence into all infirmary deaths in which any of his old enemies and rivals had been involved.

Hospital management, however, was worse still. The medical staff merely

The Radcliffe Infirmary, opened in 1770 (*Oxfordshire Health Archives*)

Small wonder there was inefficiency at the Radcliffe Infirmary – the out-patients department in 1863 (*Oxfordshire Health Archives*)

CHOLERA.

PREVENTION.

1. Let every person be washed perfectly clean, morning and evening.
2. Let every room be cleaned and swept every day, and well washed at least once a week.
3. Let no rubbish nor dirt lie about the door, nor near the house.
4. Let off all stagnant water.
5. Let the house be whitewashed with hot lime.
6. Beware of Drunkenness—nothing is so likely to bring on Disease.

If any one is seized with sickness, slight vomiting, and purging, a burning heat at the stomach, with cramp in various parts of the body, and a feeling of cold all over, it probably is the Cholera.

Advice to Families.

1. Send off instantly for the Doctor.
2. Send to   for the Medicine for the Cholera, and give the Patient a table-spoonful of the Mixture, in hot water, as under, and fifteen drops of the Oil of Peppermint in hot brandy and water.
3. If he vomits, give him another dose of each, and so on, till it stays on his stomach.
4. Warm the bed and put him into it between the blankets : you must do all you can to get warmth into him.
5. Set some water on the fire, and as soon as possible dip some flannels in it scalding, wring them out and foment the parts where the pain is felt.
6. Fill two or three quart bottles with hot water and put them to the parts where the pain is felt, and to the hands and feet.
7. If no better, let some persons rub him with dry and hot flannels wherever he feels pain.
8. Take some common flour and flour of mustard, half and half, mix it with a little hot vinegar or water ; then spread it a quarter of an inch thick on a cloth, about a foot square, and put it on his stomach, and other plasters on his hands and feet, and where he feels most pain.
9. While attending the sick, be sure not to let him breathe in your face.
10. When you leave him take care to wash your hands, face, and mouth, with clean water, mixed with vinegar.
11. Some Chloride of Lime in water, should be sprinkled about the room to prevent catching the disorder.

The Medicine proper to be kept in every family is :---

1st. The Mixture, two ounces of Laudanum to fourteen ounces of Brandy, which makes a pint of the mixture. A table-spoonful mixed with as much hot water, is a dose.
2nd. An ounce of Oil of Peppermint, or Cajeput. Fifteen drops is a dose, in a wine-glass of brandy and water.
3rd. A bottle of Chloride of Lime. A wine-glassful put into four quarts of water makes the proper Mixture for sprinkling.

Be not thou far from me, O Lord; thou art my succour haste thee to help me —Psalm 22.
Consider and hear me, O Lord my God, lighten mine eyes that I sleep not in death.—Psalm 13.
My God, haste thee to help me; forsake me not when my strength faileth me.—Psalm 71.

PRINTED BY J. MUNDAY, OXFORD.

Warning the poor to beware of the cholera, in a less than reassuring manner (*Oxfordshire Health Archives*) included incompetents; the administrative staff had at least one individual who was actively corrupt. Absalom Whiting had been secretary to the Radcliffe Infirmary's board of governors for several years when, in 1822, the first hints appear in the minutes that something odd was happening. A payment of 3 gns. was made to Mr Coke for examining the secretary's accounts, and in May William Slatter suddenly requested that 'a Committee be appointed straightway to enquire into the state of the accounts of the Infirmary'. The committee was set up at once, and the following week reported that Whiting 'had not given a satisfactory account of his transactions in the money concerns of the Infirmary'. It called for a full meeting of the board on 14 June to get the full story from the secretary.

At this point the governors had a very nasty shock. When they assembled on 14 June, they were told that Whiting had been absent from the infirmary for the past month, and rumours were circulating that he had been seen boarding a ship for America. He could certainly afford to. It turned out that since 1814, the sum of £2,140 8s. 5½d. had quietly gone missing from the infirmary funds. That sort of sum is difficult to hide, but Whiting had profited from the reluctance of nineteenth-century tradesmen to dun a respectable institution. The printed accounts of the Radcliffe showed that all its suppliers had been regularly paid; in fact, it transpired that they were owed £1,588 17s. 6s. The board decided to take firm action. They would inform the tradesmen, they resolved, that they considered themselves responsible only for payments due in that year, and 'not for any arrears previous to 31 December last'.

This time it was the tradesmen's turn to have a shock. They had not allowed extended credit to the august Radcliffe in order to be forced into bankruptcy, and they said so in no uncertain terms. Thomas Brain, a butcher, was particularly aggrieved. He was owed £120, and with a positively staggering naïvety had given Whiting a receipt for it before he was paid, thus depriving himself of any legal right to the money. In a desperate letter to the board, he denied any knowledge of Whiting's corruption: 'It is extremely hard, Gentlemen, from my being so unfortunately circumstanced as to be unacquainted with the regular forms of business accounts, that this should deprive me in your opinion of what is justly and honestly my due.'

Brain wasn't the only man to be justifying himself in frantic letters to the board. The Revd John Dean, Principal of St Mary Hall, was in a very difficult position. He was the member of the board officially responsible for the published accounts in 1821, and it was now evident that he had blithely put his name to a complete work of fiction. Shortly after the special meeting he wrote to his colleagues: 'the printed account of 1821 is disavowed by me as full of inaccuracy and misstatement, unauthorized on my part and issued in my absence, though I had repeatedly sought in vain to bring the Secretary to a personal interview for an examination and final adjustment of the account'.

But most of the letters the board received came from Whiting. They never actually managed to find him, but they did receive a constant flow of correspondence, in which he claimed to be more sinned against than sinning. In June 1824 he wrote, 'I have ever confessed my own culpable neglect and carelessness, which I could but know when known to the Governors must give them great offence, but at the same time the plan I should have followed would have been that, as not to have left anything unpaid, and the accounts fairly balanced'. He went on to speak of his 'present distress through want of money', which was rather an odd thing to say when over £2,000 remained unaccounted for. Eventually the board persuaded the tradesmen to agree to a loss of 10 per cent on the money owed to them, and turned their mind to ensuring that they could never be defrauded again. Future secretaries were to enter into a bond for £500 security against the due performance of their office. They also insisted that all holders of the post henceforth must be qualified auditors. It was probably rather stupid of them to insist on a secretary who would know exactly how to cook the books without being found out. For it is a matter of record that before long the board was comprehensively defrauded again.

One generally has very little choice about entering hospital, however suspect it is known to be. The various plagues which hit Oxford through the ages were no respecters of persons. By the nineteenth century, the authorities posted notices throughout the town warning the inhabitants of what they could expect. These were not cheering:

If anyone is seized with sickness, slight vomiting and purging, a burning heat at the stomach, with cramp in various parts of the body and a feeling of cold all over, it probably is the cholera.

To most people that would have read like a death sentence. Still, there were attempts to instruct the Oxford dwellers, particularly those in the slums, as to the precautions they could take against the disease. They were told to throw lime – distributed free – into the cess pits and houses of easement. They were instructed to whitewash their houses. Chloride of lime was recommended as a disinfectant, and R.T. Jones, a druggist in the High Street, made a metaphorical killing by becoming the town's supplier. Admittedly some of the information notices read like the soupier kind of Victorian religious tract:

Look to Godfrey's Row – look to Bull Street – and learn from their afflictions a lesson profitable to yourselves. Like you, they tarried too long in the midst of disease and, sooner than quit their habitations, many sickened and died. But some there were who sought safety for themselves and their families by removal. The Board of Health opened the doors of their house in St Aldate's to receive them, and all did well, and have since expressed their thankfulness.

The power of the message was diluted a little by the insistence of various upright citizens on slipping their own personal crusades into the warnings. If, for example, the temperance movement could link up their propaganda with the cholera notices, they might create the impression that a glass of gin was tantamount to suicide. 'Beware drunkenness – nothing is so likely to bring on disease.' In particular, the authorities wanted to do something about St Giles Fair, and this looked like the perfect opportunity; although admittedly the fair probably did help the cholera to spread:

Caution and remonstrance to all drunkards and revellers, and to the thoughtless and imprudent of both sexes. Be warned against long sittings, dancings, revellings, surfeitings and mixed, crowded companies in booths and showrooms. Many who have raised the cup in merriment to their lips, have in agony lamented their excesses, and at their deaths have left a last legacy of warning to the drunkard.

Mental health was no more free from difficulties than the physical variety. Over in the Warneford, the county's non-pauper lunatic asylum and now a respected psychiatric hospital, they had their own problems. These started with a builder who seemed to have a very sketchy understanding of the principles of competitive tendering. In 1821, the chosen architect, Richard Ingleman, invited a number of builders to submit their estimates for the job, and eventually came down in favour of Daniel Evans of Holborn in London. Unfortunately a certain Samuel Lake had not understood that he was being invited to tender for the job; he thought that he had been chosen to build the hospital, and was most incensed when he received a rejection. In a scorching letter to the chairman of the building committee, he declared himself to be 'injured in every respect', and said that 'if the agreement with the present person is not put aside and mine received, I expect to be remunerated for my trouble'. Ingleman replied that Lake's calculations were 'too low to finish the building in any thing, or in any way, to my satisfaction'. Lake returned that 'it is a fact that *myself* and I only am entitled to the erection of the building'. This was the Warneford's first case of paranoia, but they treated it by simply ignoring the man until he went away.

Their second case of mental illness centred upon the first resident director, which was unfortunate. Mr Bakewell was the son of a private madhouse keeper in Staffordshire, and was appointed in July 1826. On 4 September he was 'pronounced unfit for the situation of Superintendent, owing to his state of mind'. On 21 September Mr and Mrs Moore came to replace him, as director and matron respectively. They had gained much experience in the London madhouses, and were felt to be an excellent choice. However, what they had gained experience of was later called into question. Two years after their appointment they were dismissed for culpable conduct; Mr Moore was accused of keeping the books badly, using the premises to fatten his own pigs, and feeding the veal provided for the patients to his dog. This might explain why the Warneford under the Moores found itself in the unusual position of a hospital which was so unpopular that it actually had to advertise in the local press for patients.

Moore was sent on his way by Frederick Wintle, the resident apothecary of the hospital. Realizing that his tyrannical boss was no longer in a position to harm him, Wintle wrote to the hospital committee:

Gentlemen – In consequence of the violent abuse I received from Martha Kent, of whose conduct towards a female patient I thought it my duty to complain, and the shameful assault committed here by one of the keepers upon a tradesman a few evenings ago, I have felt it necessary to absent myself from the Asylum for a few nights. Mr Moore does screen the faults of the servants and, as it were, consents to their bad conduct, for in the case of Martha Kent he stood by and heard her malignant abuse towards me on two separate times without saying one word to reprove or dissuade her, therefore I cannot expect the least protection from him should any of the servants be disposed to assault or abuse me, which I conceive is not unlikely, as they know I am opposed to and have exposed much of their ill conduct.

The servants and keepers were about to receive an unpleasant surprise; not only did the committee support Wintle, they even appointed him and his wife to replace the Moores. There was a rapid clearing out of old staff, and the Warneford became a far more pleasant place to stay. Far from being the traditional grim madhouse keepers of fiction (and too often fact), the Wintles ran a spacious, caring institution, bringing up their children in the asylum and treating the patients very much as an extended family. One of their children later became secretary to the asylum, another played the organ there. It does no harm to remember the occasional saint among the sinners.

INSTRUCTIONS TO THE KEEPERS,

MALE AND FEMALE.

ALWAYS bear in mind that you are in your senses, and that those who are under your care are not: this is your health and happiness; that is their affliction and disease: and you cannot better shew your gratitude to God for his mercy and goodness to yourself, than by shewing kindness and consideration to these your afflicted brethren.

Be kind and gentle to them as long and as far as you can.

If you must use strong words, let them be few, and well chosen. Never speak rashly, or in a hurry.

If you must do strong things, do them firmly, but never in a passion.

If you are called upon to use main force, never strike; if you are a striker, you are not fit for your situation: striking a patient is forbidden in this House.

Never suffer yourself to be made angry by scoffs, taunts, or mockery; they are words without meaning in the mouths of those who utter them.

If a patient use threats, as well as insults, lose no time in telling the Director what has been said, and why, if you can find out any reason for it.

You are to live with your patients; this is your bounden duty, your hired service.

You are to remember, that all Insane persons kept in close confinement are crafty, at least they soon become so; for they are contriving how to get out of it.

Look well to the walls of the garden courts, the windows, wearing apparel, bed and bed clothes, and see if there be any thing done, prepared, procured, or contrived, to destroy life, or facilitate escape.

If you can do or devise any thing in the way of pastime or amusement for them, tell the Director of your device, and, if it be approved of, try it.

Do not let those who mope loiter in their bed rooms; try by persuasion to get them to walk out in the garden courts and mix with the other patients.

Do not let any of the other patients go to the violent, it makes them more violent.

In giving orders to the sullen and refractory, speak as if you were delivering a message from the Director; and generally, whenever you have any thing to do or to make them do, which you know that the patients will dislike, tell them that you are obeying your superiors, and must do your duty: this will often save you from angry or saucy replies, and from ill will.

As you are never to put a patient into the waistcoat, belt, or chair, without the Director's orders, so also without his orders you must never relieve any from these restraints; if you do so, fatal consequences may ensue either to the patient or yourself: entreaties and promises are to be reported to the Director, but you are not to act upon them without his authority.

The acceptable face of caring for the patients in the early Warneford asylum – instructions to the keepers (*Oxfordshire Health Archives*)

The unacceptable face of caring for the patients in the early Warneford asylum – restraint belt with wrist locks (*Oxfordshire Health Archives*)

The spacious and elegant grounds of the Warneford asylum (*Oxfordshire Health Archives*)

Of course, such things were relative. The Wintles were enlightened and the Warneford a humane, forward-looking hospital for the day; nevertheless, some of the methods in use there would cause a raised eyebrow or two if they were employed today. Drugs were used frequently, emetics and opiates particularly, but also arsenic, creosote and wine. Bleeding was regularly used, and bathing was a common remedial treatment. In a more sinister vein, an electrifying machine was purchased in 1830 – electric shock treatment was just coming into its own. The purchase of wrist locks, restraint chairs and hobbles all appear in the accounts. All of which sits oddly with the stories of carriage drives in the country, cricket, tennis, croquet, picnics and river parties, with indoor games, amateur theatricals and popular lectures in the winter months.

Suspect treatment being administered by the most well meaning of carers was a common occurrence in past centuries, and future ages will perhaps accuse us of the same thing. Oxfordshire Archives holds a collection of remedies and cures for various ailments, dating from the eighteenth century. They give one a healthy feeling of relief that one lives in the twentieth. To cure a sore:

Take Coventry blue thread, dipped in frogspawn.

However, it was better to have a sore, than a pain in the side:

Horse dung, squeezed in milk, and made into whey; give a quarter of a pint often.

As for a fever:

Take fresh gun ammunition, Venice soap, hog lice, purified nitre, and half a scruple of balsam. Make twenty pills, and take two morning and evening.

The point here is obviously the balsam. It turns up in a number of the prescriptions, and from the description given is obviously some sort of wonder drug:

it cures ulcers, cankers, the bite of a mad dog and all venemous creatures, smallpox, it takes away the redness and pains in the stomach, helps any sore, takes away worms, and is very good for a horse that is hurt in shoeing.

It probably cleans out the drains as well, but the writer forgot to mention it. Certainly there are more unpleasant ways of being cured of the bite of a mad dog:

> Let the patient be bloodied in the arm nine or ten times; take the herb called ash-coloured ground liverwort (half an ounce) and black pepper (two drams), mix, and take a dose for four mornings. The patient must be put into a cold bath every morning, fasting, for a month; he must be dipped all over, with his head above the water. N.B. dipping in the sea, after the manner which is usually prescribed, is of no service at all.

Beware of admitting to a weak or decaying constitution. The compiler of these recipes will finish it off:

> Take thirty garden snails in the shells, and as many red earthworms out of a gravelly soil; take the snails out of the shells and wash them, bruise the snails and cut the worms in pieces, then put them into three pints of spring water, boil, and sweeten to your taste. This cured Miss Jenkinson after being given over by seven doctors.

Actually, this probably goes to prove that a desire for revenge can give the possessor of the most decayed constitution a will to live. Miss Jenkinson should have been grateful that she didn't suffer from weak eyes into the bargain:

> Take a bit of fresh raw beef, about as big as an inch, and lay it on the nape of the neck just below the roots of the hair when going to bed; do this every night. When taken off in the morning, the beef will smell very strong.

Given the usual standards of eighteenth-century hygiene, there is little doubt that it would. Among the collection is something which simply calls itself a recipe for lunacy:

> Take three large handfuls of ground ivy, shred small, boil it in two quarts of white wine until two thirds is consumed, strain it and add six ounces of salad oil, boil it into an ointment, then shave the patient's head and rub it in. Take fresh herbs and tie them on the top of the head very hard.

What the prescription neglects to explain is whether this is supposed to cure lunacy, or merely persuade everyone that the patient meets that he is suffering from it.

A recipe for dealing with a pain in the stomach is worth pausing over:

Infuse a small handful of camomile flowers in a pint and a half of water until it reduces to a pint, then put in half a pint of strong white wine, a little toasted rhubarb, and some brandy.

There is no guarantee that it will do anything for the pain, but after that the patient probably wouldn't care any more. Most of the cures fall into the general category of unacceptable alternative medicine. When this sort of thing was taken seriously, it is hardly surprising that so many people found themselves facing their final chapter sooner than they had expected.

CHAPTER EIGHT

DEATH . . . AND BEYOND . . .

Nobody lives forever – not in the terrestrial sense, at least. Sinners and villains go the way of all flesh, frequently faster than their more law-abiding brethren, and occasionally assisted by the authorities or their even more sinful and villainous friends. But if they plan things carefully, they can have the satisfaction of leaving confusion and chaos behind them, and if the living plan carefully, they might even make something out of someone else's departure. If the departed then decide to come back, all hell can be let loose.

Funerals were where the problems often started. Out in the Forest of Wychwood, it was the custom for the outlying villages to bear the corpses of their deceased parishioners through the woods to be buried at Shipton. The villagers had their own version of a wake, as is noted by the antiquary Thomas Symonds:

> Farmers and tradesmen invite their friends and neighbours, the young and robust forming themselves into sets of bearers. But it too frequently happens that this solemn rite degenerates into scenes of debauchery and riot, the more depraved characters remaining at Shipton, drinking, quarrelling and fighting, till compelled to return to their habitations from want of money or credit. These excesses render Forest burials celebrated far around, although the abuses are confined to the rudest of the villagers.

It could be worse, and on one noted occasion it was. The funeral was that of a gentleman named Eldridge in the early eighteenth century, an

112

individual noted for being economical with the truth to such an extent that a hundred years after his death the phrase 'he is as big a liar as Old Eldridge' was still current in the area. If Eldridge had been able to tell the story of his own funeral no one would have believed it, which is a sort of poetic justice.

The procession set off through the forest from Ramsden, and was proceeding in a sober and solemn manner down to Five Ash Bottom, when suddenly one of the bearers spotted a squirrel, an unusual sight in the middle of winter. Chasing squirrels was a favourite sport, and the bearers felt sure that Eldridge would have appreciated a good squirrel chase as much as the next man, so they dropped the corpse and set off after it. It was a very fit squirrel, and led them half way across the forest before vanishing into a walled coppice just as night was falling. Naturally this was a bit of a disappointment, and they were just about to retire to the nearest hostelry to commiserate with one another, when someone remembered that when they had set out that morning they had had a coffin with them.

It was at this point that the blizzard started. The bearers soon realized that if they didn't find shelter soon they would probably be joining Eldridge, so they battled their way to the nearest village and holed up for the night. The next morning they were up bright and early to look for the coffin, but unfortunately the forest was under a foot of snow, and no one could remember exactly where they had put it down. It took three days to find Eldridge's body, which fortunately was in very good condition, having been in the equivalent of a deep freeze. It couldn't have happened to a more appropriate man.

At least Eldridge had a grave waiting for him when he finally reached the churchyard. Mrs Horseman of Holton, who died in 1630, was denied a place in consecrated ground and invited to apply to the nearest crossroads. The problem was that she died excommunicate, which meant that she was not eligible to receive Christian burial. Edward Powell of Forest Hill sent to Dr Barker, the official of the diocese, asking for a faculty specifically allowing her to be buried, but Barker sent back a refusal, and 'when the messenger brought word it would not be granted, he did advise Edward Day and another of his servants dwelling at Wheatley to bury her in the garden'. The idea of interring granny among the lupins did not appeal to the family, so they tried a different tack. Powell firmly denied that he had tried to bribe the diocesan officer into handing out a faculty on the quiet, or that he had had a similar conversation with Mr Price, the rector of Holton, but the rector's son Bartholemew recalled otherwise:

Edward Day and Thomas Day and John Robins and John Stay came to his father to entreat him to suffer Mrs Horseman to be buried, and if he did so Edward Powell of Forest Hill would bear him out, if it cost a hundred pounds.

The rector would not give way, however big the bribe. He knew full well that the odds were on his side; he could go on stonewalling for as long as he liked, but the Powell contingent had a very limited time to get permission for churchyard burial, even though it was the middle of winter. Mary Slyman of Wheatley summed it up:

> Mrs Horseman died on Friday morning, on New Year's Eve, and was kept in the parlour of her house in Wheatley from that time until Monday, both day and night, albeit she was put into a coffin on New Year's Day, yet by Monday she began to smell so strong that they could not endure her in the house, whereupon on Monday at night they drew her corpse in her coffin out into the garden, and the next morning drew her into the parlour again, and continued this course until Wednesday, and left her in the garden on Wednesday night. . . .

When they came to draw her into the parlour again on Thursday they had a shock. Mrs Horseman had gone missing in the night. The news quickly got around, and the inference was fairly plain. Someone had buried the body quietly at night, and the apparent disturbance of the flagstones by the altar of Holton church gave the rector a good idea where. Yet he could hardly go digging for an unauthorized body, nor could he actually prove who had done it, although he took a number of people to the Church court in an attempt to do so. For all the proof I can find to the contrary she is there to this day, though it would be difficult to trace the exact spot; the burial party was not so tactless as to leave a memorial tablet.

Sixty years later, Samuel Shenton, the vicar of Wallingford, was much more cunning in dealing with a burial he didn't want. He had a long-term problem with William Blackhall's family, who were much given to attending dissenting meeting houses in preference to his church. However, since the family kept a low profile and paid their tithes regularly there wasn't a great deal he could do – until the day that Mary, William's wife, died.

Now Shenton could simply have tried refusing her burial, but that would have been too easy. There was an odd situation with the churches in Wallingford at this time, and Shenton saw how he could turn it to his advantage. He was the vicar of two churches, St Mary's and St Peter's, but the latter was effectively derelict. All the inhabitants of St Peter's parish had the right to attend St Mary's church and to be buried in the churchyard there. This should have been of no concern to the Blackhall family, who lived in St Mary's parish and already had a child buried in that churchyard, but it became a major strand in Shenton's plan to get every member of the Blackhall clan out of St Mary's churchyard for good.

His first move was to claim that there was no room for another burial in St Mary's, and that William's wife would have to be buried at St Peter's. William was inclined to kick up a fuss about this, but his dissenting background meant that he was fighting from a weak position, and he reluctantly gave way, making the official request to have a grave dug in the name of Blackhall at St Peter's and paying the requisite fees. This was precisely what Shenton wanted. No sooner was the grave finished than Shenton dashed back to St Mary's with his little band of gravediggers and found a Blackhall to put in it, to wit, William's little child. He dug up the body, ran it down to St Peter's, and filled in the grave on top of it, secure in the bureaucratic knowledge that William had ordered a grave for a Blackhall to be buried in, and William had got precisely that.

One hour later, Mary's funeral procession arrived at St Peter's churchyard to find no grave and the churchyard gates locked. Shenton refused to open the gates on the pretext that he wasn't expecting a funeral, and William had no option but to bury his wife in a nearby field. He was not awfully happy about this and dragged Shenton before the bishop for conduct unbefitting a clergyman, but Shenton claimed his conscience was clear. No one had told him which Blackhall the grave was intended for, and Mary's corpse had not been brought for a funeral service to the church but to the local meeting house, from which he might reasonably have concluded that the burial was to be at the dissenters' cemetery. The argument was tenuous in the extreme, but the dissenters were far from popular at the time and Shenton made it stick. He went back to his nice, dissenter-free churchyard of St Mary's and remained there as vicar until his death, many years later.

The best chance most deceased persons have of getting their own back on those who outlive them is through their wills. Many a surviving relative has met with an unpleasant shock in the lawyer's office after the funeral, and a number of them have gone on to make the lawyer's day by contesting the will. In 1737 John Hedges, a lawyer himself, decided that his fellow toilers in the courts were not going to make any money out of him, and not content with this shocking lack of professional solidarity, rubbed it in by writing his will in verse:

> The fifth day of May
> Being airy and gay
> And to hyp. not inclined
> But of vigorous mind

And my body in health
I'll dispose of my wealth
And all I'm to leave
On this side of the grave
To some one or other
And I think to my brother
Because I forsaw
That my brethren in law
If I did not take care
Would come in for their share
Which I nowise intended
Till their manners are mended.
(And of that, God knows, there's no sign)
I do therefore enjoin
And do strictly command
Of which witness my hand
That nought I have got
Be brought into hotch-pot
But I give and devise
As much as in me lies
To the son of my mother
My own dear brother
To have and to hold
All my silver and gold
As the affectionate pledges
Of his brother,

John Hedges

To the inexperienced eye, some wills appear even odder than Hedges'. It was not always possible for a dying man or woman to write, or even sign or set a mark to their last will and testament; at times it was all they could do to gasp out their final wishes to nearby witnesses, who would then be required to swear in court that their testimony genuinely represented those dying words. Instead of the traditional 'In the name of God, amen. I do make my last will and testament . . .' which would normally be found, the will consists of a more or less convoluted story told by the witnesses, which can give a delightful picture of the subject's final moments on earth. Many record offices can provide an example of a will which has obviously been bellowed through a window by a man dying of some contagious disease to witnesses in the street who have no intention of getting close enough to allow him to sign. The will of Robert Danbe of Iffley provides a wonderful picture of the potential beneficiaries falling out not in the lawyer's office, but before the will was actually completed.

John Watson, a farmer of Iffley, took his oath that at about three o'clock in the morning on Monday 6 April 1789, he was sent for by Robert Danbe, who asked him to bring in witnesses including a Mr Brown. Danbe asked Brown to write his will for him, for he should not live five minutes. Brown declined, so Danbe turned to Watson and asked him, but Watson said he had no idea how to go about it, and recommended that an attorney be sent for. All this must have been greatly frustrating for a man on the point of giving up the ghost, but Danbe agreed to the attorney and a message was duly sent. Nevertheless, it was obvious that Danbe was unlikely to last long enough to talk to the attorney, so Watson reluctantly agreed to take dictation. Danbe began, 'I give my wife all my goods and chattels', when Watson, eying the heavily pregnant Mrs Danbe, observed that 'something was coming' and provision should be made. Danbe agreed, and Watson wrote in a series of clauses ensuring that the child would benefit from its father's estate and be well looked after. They sorted out an estate Danbe had recently purchased, and the executors, then Watson finished off the will ready for signing.

At this point Miss Danbe, Danbe's sister, came in to the room. She picked the will up from the bed, and a quick glance was enough to show her who was conspicuous by her absence. With commendable presence of mind, she headed down the stairs with it, but never managed to reach the ground floor as Mrs Danbe got to her, and after a scuffle gained possession of the document, slipped it inside her dress to protect it, and brought it back to her dying husband. She made great complaint to her husband of how she had been treated by his sister, and produced the will, only for Danbe to point out, 'My dear, this is of no use unless I put my hand to it'. He called for pen and ink, which then had to be found and brought, then: 'he took the pen in his hand and attempted to write his name to his will, and whilst he was making the first letter of his name at the bottom of the will, fell back and expired immediately.'

It seemed that Miss Danbe had achieved her aim by delay, but not so. Watson and the witnesses went into court and told the whole story; the will, though unsigned and in Watson's handwriting, was passed as genuine, and Mrs Danbe and the child were confirmed in their property. It does seem a bit hard on Miss Danbe though.

Of course, the great problem with a will is that the one person qualified to say exactly what the testator meant is in no position to comment on the matter; not unless he can find some way of coming back from the grave. In fact, a number of Oxfordshire inhabitants have succeeded in doing precisely that, and have discovered no less than three ways of achieving it. The first involves outside help, and has the disadvantage that although you get out of the grave as such, you remain just as dead as when you were in it.

At the time when the grisly activities of Messrs Burke and Hare were sending a chill through the nation, Oxfordshire had its own Resurrection Men – Davis and Tyrrell. The two were rivals rather than partners; Tyrrell was a loner, while Davis had a couple of cronies called Bedgood and Knapp. What they had in common was incompetence. They both got caught. The Davis team was quite astonishingly stupid, as it went in for stealing bodies from their own parish of Caversham, which was asking for trouble. Tyrrell avoided his own patch, where he was known, and was actually arrested for body-snatching in Broughton, where in 1831 he was accused of digging open a grave in the churchyard and *having in his possession* the dead body of one Mary Anne Roberts. That has a slightly sinister ring to it, but probably means that he walked out of the churchyard with it over one shoulder and straight into the arms of a waiting constable.

The Resurrection Men found a market because the usual supply of bodies for the anatomy schools was too slow. There was usually a steady stream of executed criminals from the gallows, who were handed over to the surgeons so that they could at least perform a valuable service to society after they were dead, even if they had shown a reluctance to do so while they were alive. It was one of these criminals who pioneered the second way of coming back from the grave: rising from the dead.

Anne Greene was a maidservant who was unfortunate enough to catch the eye of Jeoffrey Reade, the grandson of Sir Thomas Reade of Duns Tew. In the traditional way of such stories, after a brief liaison she found that she was pregnant and in due course gave birth to an illegitimate child. Nor was her way of dealing with the problem all that out of the ordinary; she smothered the baby, and was brought to trial for murder. Found guilty, she was hanged in the Castle Yard at Oxford on 14 December 1649. So far her story was in no way extraordinary. What happened next made it the sensation of the day.

As was usual, her body was taken down, beaten with the butt end of a musket and stamped on repeatedly to ensure that she was dead. It was then taken off to the Anatomy School – at that time sited in that part of what is now the Bodleian Library adjoining the south staircase – for dissection. Just as Dr Petty, the reader in anatomy, was about to use his scalpel, he noticed that the body was still unusually warm. With the help of his fellow physicians he set about reviving her, and eventually brought her back to consciousness. She was at first unable to speak, giddy, and badly bruised by the rope, but within a few days these signs had faded. Petty had brought in several women to look after her, but as her powers of speech returned he saw a danger; the women were more than curious about what she had experienced when she was apparently dead, and had begun to question her about it. He quickly had her quarantined, to prevent loose talk from getting around.

Petty was more curious than anyone, and the moment he had got rid of the audience he started to cross-question her himself. To his annoyance she appeared completely incoherent. When he spoke of her miraculous deliverance from her sufferings, she replied that she hoped God would give her the patience to endure it. Eventually he gave up trying to make sense of her wanderings. It was not until the following day that he realized what had happened.

Anne Greene had simply lost three days from her life. The contemporary broadsheet *Mercurius Politicus* reported:

> She affirmed, and doth still, that she neither remembereth how her fetters were knocked off, how she went out of the prison, when she was turned off the ladder, whether any psalm was sung or not, nor was she sensible of any pain, as she can remember. And being told that she spoke very well and pertinently on the gallows such and such words, she confessed that she did not remember to have said them there, but that she resolved the day before to speak to that purpose.
>
> Another thing observable is, that she came to herself as if she had awakened out of sleep, not recovering the use of speech by slow degrees, but in a manner altogether, beginning to speak just where she had left off on the gallows, concerning Sir Thomas Reade's house and the lewdness thereof.

Anne married, had a legitimate family, and lived into old age, but she was never able to remember, however much people pleaded with her, just what she had experienced between stepping off the gallows and coming to in the Anatomy School.

Petty was the hero of the hour, and his reputation was made. This was distinctly irksome to a number of his fellow physicians, who felt that he had been lucky rather than skilful. Anyone could make a reputation with a near-dead victim of the gallows; all it needed was for the hangman to be careless again. It was bound to happen. They waited. It took ten years, but at last they got their chance.

On 4 May 1659 another maid was hanged at Green Ditch for precisely the same crime as her famous predecessor. Her body was delivered into the hands of Dr Conyers of St John's College, and at once he realized that his time had come. With the help of his young colleagues he brought the latest victim round and back into full consciousness, ready to announce his triumph to the world. Unfortunately he had reckoned without Henry Mallory and the other bailiffs of the town. Conyers was concerned with expanding the boundaries of science; Mallory was far more interested in the punishment of villains. He'd already lost Anne Greene, who was out there somewhere leading an enjoyable life instead of lying in numerous pieces six feet under. Now it looked like he was going to lose another one.

It never occurred to Conyers that he ought to do something about protecting his protégée. Shortly after midnight the bailiffs attacked the house where she was resting; they broke down the door, bundled her into a coffin, and carried her out to the field of Broken Hayes, now lost beneath the Gloucester Green bus station. Having a shrewd idea of what was in their minds, their victim was heard crying out, 'Lord, have mercy upon me!', but this did not prevent them from lynching her on the nearest tree, and making sure that the job was done properly this time. Mallory obviously reckoned he had done his duty, but he was a poor judge of popular psychology. The hatred he attracted by his action led to his being abused whenever he walked down the street. He was cursed by the women of the town. Eventually his cutler's business went bankrupt, which was attributed to the curses heaped upon him, though it doesn't take an economist to see that a shop which no one patronizes won't last long. Meanwhile the inhabitants of Oxford, with a fine disdain for ecology, cut down the offending tree.

There is no record of Anne Greene's successor making a second reappearance. Yet for the third category of Oxfordshire inhabitants the minor inconvenience of being dead has not deterred them from dropping round for a chat with their friends. In the burial register of Souldern there is an account of the experience of Geoffrey Shaw, rector of the parish at the beginning of the eighteenth century, which he related to a friend of his shortly before his death. I can do no better than to let it speak for itself:

About the end of last summer, 1706, Mr Grove, a fellow of St John's College Cambridge and Public Registrar of the University, was in the country at Souldern with his old friend Mr Geoffrey Shaw, lately fellow of St John's, who was presented by the college to the rectory, where he resided. While Mr Grove tarried with him, which was some four or five days, he told him this remarkable story. Namely, that some days before as he was sitting in his study late at night, and while he was smoking tobacco and reading, the spectre of his old companion Mr Nailor, who died about five years ago in St John's College, came into the room, habited in a gown and cassock and exactly in the same

St George's Tower, one of the last remnants of old Oxford castle and gaol (*Oxfordshire Archives*)

The Schools Quadrangle of the Bodleian in the seventeenth century, where Anne Greene was brought back to life in 1649 (*Oxfordshire Archives*)

Brasenose Lane in the nineteenth century, where Vice-Principal Churton watched the devil drag a student off to hell (*Centre for Oxfordshire Studies*)

Woodstock Palace, plagued by the devil after the execution of Charles I in 1649 (*Centre for Oxfordshire Studies*)

manner as he used to appear in the college when he was alive. Mr Shaw remembered the figure well, and was therefore much surprised. But the spectre took a chair and, sitting down close to him, bid him not to be afraid for he came to acquaint him with something which nearly concerned him.

So, entering into discourse, he told him that their friend Mr Orchard was to die very suddenly, and that he himself should die soon after him, and that he therefore came to forewarn him, that he might prepare himself accordingly. After this, they talked of many other things, for their conference lasted about two hours, and amongst the rest Mr Shaw asked him if one might form some sort of notion of the other world from anything one sees in this. He answered, 'No', without giving him any further satisfaction to the question. Upon this, Mr Shaw said, 'How is it with you?' His answer was, 'I am very well and happy'. Mr Shaw asked him further whether any of his old acquaintance were with him. His answer was that there was not one of them, which answer, Mr Shaw said, struck him to the heart. At last, after two hours' conference together, the spectre took his leave, and, Mr Shaw desiring him to stay longer, he told him that he could not, for he had only three days allotted him to be absent, and they were almost expired. Mr Shaw desired that he might see him at least once more before his death, but he told him that it could not be, and so left him. After this, Mr Shaw walked about the room a considerable time, musing upon what had happened.

Still, if one has to be given notice of one's own death, the best messenger is one whose very presence proves it is nothing to be afraid of. Up to this point Shaw had been a noted scoffer when the subject of ghosts was brought up, but afterwards he was not so sure. He told the story around his college to ensure there were plenty of witnesses before the event, particularly after his friend Orchard was found dead in his chair while his servant had gone to fetch his supper. Shaw was unable to use the point to illustrate his new-found belief in ghosts for long. As he was taking evening prayer on Sunday 17 November 1706, while reading 1 Timothy 6, he fell down dead in his own church, thereby taking hold of the eternal life to which he was called.

According to the useful antiquary Symonds, Shaw was not the first clergyman to find himself conversing with the dead in Oxfordshire, by a margin of more than a thousand years. If, that is, one applies such a prosaic term as clergyman to the great St Augustine (the first Archbishop of Canterbury, not the one who wrote the *Confessions*), or credits the suspiciously apocryphal sounding story which Symonds relates. Nevertheless, *si non e vero, e ben trovato*.

About the year 600, Augustine coming to preach at Cometon in Oxfordshire, the priest of the place complained to him that, notwithstanding his frequent admonitions, the lord of the manor would pay him no tithes. [These must have been about the earliest tithes in Britain, but Augustine himself is said to have been the first man to claim the payment in England.] Augustine reproving the lord for this neglect of his devotion, he answered that the tenth sheaf belonged to him as much as the other nine, and therefore he would pay none. Augustine immediately denounced him excommunicated, and, turning to the altar to say mass, forbade any excommunicate person to be present at it; when suddenly a corpse, that lay interred at the church door, arose out of his grave and, departing out of the limits of the churchyard, stayed there during the celebration of the mass. After mass was ended, Augustine came to the man who was newly risen from the grave, and charged him in the name of God to declare who he was. The man told Augustine that in the time of the Britons he was *huius villa patronus*, and although the priest had frequently urged him to pay his tithes, he could never persuade him to comply, for which crime he said that he departed excommunicate and was carried to hell.

Augustine then asked where the priest that had excommunicated him lay interred, and being shown the place by the man who was newly risen, he called to him and bid him arise also because they wanted his help. When the priest made his appearance, Augustine asked him if he knew the other man, to which he answered that he knew him well, but wished he had never known him; 'for,' says he, 'he was always an enemy to the Church, refused to pay his tithes, continued a great sinner till his death, and therefore I excommunicated him.' Augustine then declared that it was fit to show mercy towards him, wherefore he absolved him and sent him to his grave, where he fell again into dust and ashes. When he was departed, the priest who was newly restored to life told Augustine that he had been interred there above 170 years, and when Augustine would have persuaded him to continue upon earth for the instruction of souls, he absolutely refused to consent, so he also returned to his grave. The lord of the place, standing by all the while and trembling, was asked if he would now pay his tithes; he instantly fell down at Augustine's feet, weeping and confessing his crime, and, being absolved, continued during the remainder of his life a diligent follower of Augustine.

A case of careless talk saving lives? I remain unconvinced. Long-dead corpses walking around in the church are one thing, but no historian could feel entirely comfortable with the suggestion that a formal system of tithes existed in this country as early as AD 430. By contrast, surely no former Brasenose man could fail to hear a ring of truth in the story of the apparition at the college Hellfire Club. I first heard a garbled version of the story as an undergraduate in the mid-1970s, but it was not until I was in a position to get hold of the relevant archives that the definitive story was made clear.

The Brasenose Hellfire Club flourished in the 1820s, composed mainly of members of the college (though with four or five men from other colleges), and modelled on the more famous Hellfire Club of Wilkes and Dashwood in the eighteenth century – or at least on what that older club was believed to have been; vice, drunkenness and aggressive atheism were its hallmarks. The college authorities, being by no means stupid, were well aware of its existence and the names of most of its members, but however much they might disapprove, there was very little they could do about it unless some flagrant breach of university discipline occurred.

As today, the north wall of the college formed one side of Brasenose Lane, which has changed little over the years beyond the addition of bicycle racks, and is still a rather gloomy, lonely place after dark. The college wall rises sheer, opposite the dead wall enclosing the garden of Exeter College; two levels of identical windows are topped by a third, slightly later level of gabled dormers, and the lower windows are barred to discourage the inhabitants of the rooms from leaving or entering the college by any route other than the lodge gate. In addition, the ground-floor windows had stout wire netting twisted around the bars, so that it was impossible to push so much as a hand through them.

This was the background against which the Revd T.T. Churton, Vice-Principal and Fellow of the college, made his way down the lane one evening in December, just before the end of term. It was approaching midnight and fairly dark, as the lane has never been lit by more than one or two lamps. Nevertheless, Churton thought he could make out a figure standing by one of the ground-floor windows, a tall man, apparently wrapped in a long cloak. A few steps further and he was able to identify the window; it belonged to the rooms of an undergraduate who was known to be one of the foremost members of the Hellfire Club. The tall figure seemed to be helping someone to clamber out through the window, and Churton speeded up his pace. Sneaking out of college after the lodge gate was locked was a serious offence, and this might give him the opportunity to discipline one of the more notorious members of Brasenose. Suddenly, however, he was struck with a clammy terror, as something very obvious occurred to him.

It simply wasn't possible to get out of those ground-floor windows. Even if the wire netting had been ripped off, the iron bars were set too closely together for a body to pass between them. Yet a body was clearly emerging through the window, and as Churton closed in he could see that both bars and netting were firmly in place. He could also see the tall figure on the pavement more clearly, and something about it gave him an imperative desire to be anywhere else but in this deserted lane with it. Instead of collaring the figure as he had intended, he dashed past the scene, but not so quickly that he couldn't recognize the distorted face of the undergraduate, screaming as he was forced through the bars.

Churton dashed round the corner into Radcliffe Square and hammered on the lodge gate, half-collapsing with shock. Just as the porter opened the gate, there was a tremendous cry from one of the staircases on the right hand side of Old Quad, the rooms which looked out on to Brasenose Lane, and members of the Hellfire Club came tumbling out into the night. They were minus their president for the occasion, the young undergraduate whom Churton had seen being dragged out of the window by the tall stranger. On entering his rooms, the porter found him lying dead on the floor. According to the other members of the club, he had been half way through a blasphemous oration when he had burst a blood vessel and fallen dead at their feet.

The story sounds as if it belongs in M.R. James. Interestingly, however, Falconer Madan, one of the college historians, records that the president of the Hellfire Club did die of delirium tremens about that time. What Churton saw, of course, only he knew. He was the only witness to the figure in Brasenose Lane. By contrast, there were numerous witnesses to the events in Woodstock in 1649, but to this day there remains uncertainty about what was responsible for them. The victims of the affair were in no doubt; they attributed the whole business to the devil.

It seems appropriate to conclude a survey of Oxfordshire's sinners and villains with the biggest sinner and villain of them all, on one of his periodic visits to the place. Before Blenheim, there was Woodstock Park. The King's manor house stood on the site later to be occupied by the Marlborough family, and had an interesting history into the bargain; Henry I kept his menagerie of exotic beasts there, Henry II spent a good deal of time there visiting Fair Rosamund Clifford, and Princess Elizabeth was imprisoned in the gatehouse in 1554. In 1649, however, it became abruptly surplus to requirements when its owner lost his head on the scaffold. The parliamentary commissioners set up to survey the property of the late Charles I moved into the building with their servants on 13 October that year, and took up residence in the King's own suite, making his bedchamber into their kitchen, the council hall into a brew house, the chamber of presence into an office for conducting business, and the dining room into a storehouse for wood – which they needed, as they had uprooted the King's oak in the park and chopped it up against the forthcoming winter. They were soon to regret their choice of lodging.

Various rooms had been set aside as bedchambers, and it was into one of these, on 16 October, that a large dog came wandering, snuffled around under the beds, and gnawed some of the bedcords. There was nothing unusual about this by the standards of seventeenth-century housekeeping, but when the commissioners came to look at the damage the next morning, they found the cords whole and untouched; moreover, they noticed that a quarter of beef left on a platter on the floor had been completely ignored, and they began to wonder just what sort of a dog they had in the house.

The following evening the commissioners and their servants had gone to bed and put out the lights, when they heard something come into the room. Suddenly the feet of their beds – solid four-posters – were lifted high in the air and allowed to drop with such force that many of them were flung on to the floor. This was obviously no dog, and the following evening whatever it was returned to the bedchambers with a warming pan and 'made so much a noise, that they thought five bells could not have made more'. By this time it had them badly frightened; on the 19th it began to get dangerous. One of the commissioners, more phlegmatic than the rest, who had managed to get to sleep, was awakened by someone violently shaking his shoulder; when he stuck his head through the bed curtains to find out what was going on, someone – or something – threw a trencher at it. The next night a hail of trenchers was joined by a shower of pewter dishes, and a sound like someone throwing armfuls of wood out of the dining-room, but in the morning it seemed that nothing had been moved.

The commissioners decided that they had to make a stand or be driven out of the house. One of them had the bright idea of importing their own dog into the bedchamber, and sure enough the night of the 21st passed peacefully. But by the following evening their unwanted guest had got the dog sized up, and the unfortunate creature spent the night whining and yelping. Having got the dog where it wanted it, the Devil of Woodstock, as it was now called, began in earnest. It sent showers of bricks crashing down the chimney, tugged the bed curtains to and fro, and spread broken glass about the room. What was particularly worrying was that from the earliest days the commissioners had locked all the doors in the house and kept the keys, but this did not appear to inconvenience their visitor in the least. Indeed, he extended his operations to the outside of the house.

Dreadful crashes like thunder, or the firing of cannons, were heard in the grounds of the house, and by many inhabitants of the county for some 16 miles around. On the 29th the candles went out by themselves about midnight and something could be heard striding majestically through the room, opening and shutting the windows; huge stones were thrown violently into the room, some of them landing on the beds. Giles Sharp, the secretary to the commissioners, who slept in another room, came rushing in with his sword drawn and very nearly killed one of his employers, thinking that he was the nocturnal visitor. Then the 'Devil' decided to reverse his tactics; instead of extinguishing the candles before getting down to business, he let them burn.

On the first of November, the most dreadful scene of all ensued. Candles in every part of the room were lighted, and a great fire made; at midnight, the candles all yet burning, a noise like the burst of a cannon was heard in the room, and the burning billets were tossed about by it even into their Honours' beds, who called Giles and his companions to their help, otherwise the house had been burned to the ground. About an hour after, the candles went out as usual, the crack of many cannons was heard, and many pailsful of green, stinking water were thrown upon their Honours' beds; great stones were also thrown in as before, the bed curtains and bedsteads torn and broken, the windows shattered and the whole neighbourhood alarmed with the most dreadful noises, nay, the very rabbit stealers that were abroad that night in the warren were so terrified that they fled for fear and left their ferrets behind them.

One of their Honours this night spoke and in the name of God asked what it was and why it disturbed them so? No answer was given to this, but the noise ceased for a while, when the spirit came again and, as they all agreed, brought with it seven devils worse than itself. One of the servants now lighted a large candle and set it in a doorway, between the two chambers, to see what passed, and as he watched it he plainly saw a hoof striking the candle and candlestick into the middle of the room, and afterwards, making three scrapes over the snuff, scraped it out. Upon this, the same person was so bold as to draw a sword, but he had scarcely got it out when he felt another invisible hand had got hold of it too, and pulled with him for it, and at length prevailing, struck him so violently on the head with the pummel that he fell down for dead with the blow.

At that instant was heard another burst, like the discharge of the broadside of a ship of war, and at about a minute or two's distance each, no less than nineteen more such. These shook the house so violently that they expected every moment it would fall upon their heads. The neighbours, being all alarmed, flocked to the house in great numbers, and all joined in prayer and psalm singing, during which the noise still continued in the other rooms, and the discharge of cannons was heard as from without, though no visible agent was seen to discharge them.

This would have been enough to scare off most men, but the commissioners were made of sterner stuff. What finally got to them was much simpler. They had made a quiet agreement among themselves to send back a report on the property omitting various items which were easily convertible into cash, which they would then share out among themselves. The formal agreement was signed – as they did not trust one another – and hidden under the earth in a pot with an orange tree growing in it. To their horror, while transacting business one day, they saw the earth in the pot catch fire and begin to burn with a blue smoke and an intolerable stench; they fled from the house, and this time their nerve was broken. They never returned.

Was it the Devil? There is a simpler explanation. What the commissioners didn't know was that there was no such person as Giles Sharp. The man they had hired as their secretary was Joseph Collins of Oxford, popularly known as Funny Joe, and a keen Royalist. With an inside knowledge of the secret passages of Woodstock House, a few chemical preparations, and the aid of his fellow servants, he was able to put on a creditable show of a haunting, and wreak some sort of revenge on those who had dispossessed the King. Yet Plot, in whose *Natural History of Oxfordshire* this catalogue of vice and villainy in the county began, has the last word:

> Though tricks have been often played in affairs of this kind, many of the things related are not reconcilable with juggling, such as the loud noises, beyond the power of man to make without such instruments as were not there, the tearing and breaking of the beds, the throwing about of the fire, the hoof treading out the candle. . . .

It all depends which kind of sinners and villains you prefer. The ones who live next door, or the ones who turn up on your doorstep after nightfall.

NOTES

Abbreviations
OA: Oxfordshire Archives
BNC: Brasenose College Archives
Bod: Bodleian Library
PRO: Public Record Office
OHA: Oxfordshire Health Archives

1. Father to the Man
Bletchingdon tree, Plot *Natural History of Oxfordshire*; Johnson, *OA QS Ep 1727*; Stocker, *OA MS Oxf Dioc pp c91 f131*; Savage, *OA QS Ea 1693*; Smith, *OA MS Oxf Dioc pp c94 f77*; Henley cat, *OA MS Oxf Dioc pp c4 f65v*; Johns, *OA MS Oxf Dioc pp c2 f184v*; Peppard, *OA MS Oxf Dioc pp c433*; Vaughan Thomas, *OA DD Par Yarnton b17/1*; Fettiplace, *OA MS Oxf Archd pp c160 ff265–76*.

2. Sex and Marriage
Insults, *OA MS Oxf Dioc pp c94 f82 & 104*; Jorden, *OA MS Oxf Dioc pp c26 ff11 et seq*; Nicholls, *OA MS Oxf Dioc pp c91 f101 & c42 ff37, 106, 140*; Apothecary's daughter, *Ox Hist Soc Vol. 65*; Piggott, *OA MS Oxf Dioc pp c25 ff79–80*; Giles, *OA CPZ 1*; Black Moll, *OA QS Tr 1697*; Fortnam, *OA MS Oxf Dioc pp b26 ff523 et seq*; Cawley, *OA QS Ea 1707*; Rutter, *OA MS Oxf Dioc pp c91 ff80 et seq*; Pemerton, *OA MS Oxf Dioc pp c96 ff177 et seq*; Godfrey, *OA QS Ea 1707*; Staniford, *OA MS Oxf Dioc pp c91 f57, c93 f83, Archd c14, Wills 86/2/19 & 120/3/26*; Wife sale, *OA MS Oxf Archd pp c162 ff107–8*.

3. University Rag
St Scholastica, *OA Symonds MSS*; Bodleian, Ashmole, Merton, *Oxoniana* printed for Richard Phillips, copy in OA; Barker & Sykes, *OA MS Oxf Dioc pp c91 ff301 et seq, c94 ff112 et seq*; Bathurst, *Oxoniana*; Washington, BNC 'Brazen Nose' May 1919, Nov 1923 & Nov 1924.

NOTES

4. Clerical Error

Wilberforce, *OA MS Oxf Dioc pp d178 & d550*; Ballard, *OA MS Oxf Dioc pp c650 f1*; Waldron, *OA MS Oxf Dioc pp c655 f73 et seq*; Welchman, *OA MS Oxf Dioc pp c651 ff56–61 & c652 ff52–3*; Ford, *OA MS Oxf Dioc pp c91 f206*; Quakers in gaol, *OA MS Oxf Dioc pp c650*; Betteris, *Bod Wood 515, Towner MSS Vol. 338*; Fell, *OA MS Oxf Dioc pp c430*; Banbury, *OA MS Oxf Dioc pp c94 ff98 et seq*; Lee, *OA Combe I/1*; Leigh, *OA MS Oxf Dioc pp d553*; Griffith, *OA MS Oxf Dioc pp c26 ff340 et seq*; Palmer, *OA MS Oxf Dioc pp c657*; Corbett, *OA Symonds MSS*; Gould, *OA MS Oxf Dioc pp d178 & d550*; Kening, *William Wing Annals of North Aston*; Davis, *OA MS Oxf Dioc pp c91 ff190 et seq*; King, *OA MS DD Par St Peter le Bailey c1*; Wood, *OA MS Oxf Dioc pp c94 ff145–54*; Martin, *OA Episcopat 206 box 3 bundle 4*; St Mary's church, *Oxoniana*.

5. Covington: the Arch Villain?

OA Wi VI/iv

6. Criminal Practice

Coxeter, *OA MS Oxf Dioc pp c92 f103 & c96 ff181–6*; Kembar, *OA QS Ea 1690*; Election, *Jackson's Oxford Journal 1754*; Jordan, *OA QS Trin 1696*; Boice, *OA QSM I/1*; Wolvercote, *Jackson's Oxford Journal 1829–30*, quoted in Mary Prior *Fisher's Row*; Blandy, OA pamphlets 'A genuine account of that most inhuman murder committed by Miss Mary Blandy upon the Body of her Father', 'The Tryal of Miss Mary Blandy', 'A letter from a Clergyman to Miss Mary Blandy', 'A candid appeal to the public concerning the case of the late Miss Mary Blandy', 'Miss Mary Blandy's own account of the affair between Her and Mr Cranstoun'; Kalabergo, *OA QSP I/1, Jackson's Oxford Journal 1852*, PRO Assize records; Budd, *Berks QS 1837*; Croke, Wood *Athenae* Vol. ii p. 576; Kidlington tree, Plot *Natural History of Oxfordshire*; Thame gaol, *OA QS T 1723 & Ep 1726*; Pearpoint, *OA QS Ep 1693*; Poor prisoners, *OA QS Ep 1691*; Doswell, *OA QS 1832*; Wisdom, *OA QS Mich 1786*; Harris, *OA CPZ3*.

7. Looking Very Unhealthy

All stories except remedies and cures from OHA; many quoted in AHT Robb-Smith *Short History of the Radcliffe Infirmary*, A.G. Gibson *The Radcliffe Infirmary*, Brenda Parry-Jones *The Warneford Hospital Oxford*. Whiting, *RI 1C1/5, RI II/100/10, WP 5(xliii)*; Cholera, *RI I/15*; Lake, *WP 5(xxvi), WP 26(xv)*; Bakewell, *WV 212(i)*; Moore, *WV 213(i)*; Wintles, *W Add 206(iii), WV 148(i), Annual Reports*; Remedies, *OA Infofile copies*.

8. Death . . . and Beyond . . .
Shipton funeral, *OA Symonds MSS*; Horseman, *OA MS Oxf Dioc pp c2 f 144 et seq*; Wallingford, *OA MS Oxf Dioc pp c94 f127*; Doctors Commons, *Jackson's Oxford Journal* 1737; Danbe, *OA MS Wills Oxon 100.141*; Resurrection Men, *OA QS Ep 1830, Jackson's Oxford Journal* 1831; Green, *OA Symons MSS*; Souldern ghost, *OA MS DD Par Souldern*; Comerton ghost, *OA Symonds MSS*; Brasenose ghost, *BNC uncat papers*; Devil of Woodstock, *OA Symonds MSS,* Plot *Natural History of Oxfordshire.*

INDEX OF PLACES

131